Are you interested in

a course management system that would

save you time & effort?

If the answer is *yes*, **CourseCompass is for you.**

Contact your local
Allyn & Bacon/Longman
sales representative
for a free access code, or
visit www.coursecompass.com,
and take a tour of this course
management system.

Technical support
is available for
faculty and students:
support@coursecompass.com
1-800-677-6337

CourseCompass is an online course management system
designed to help you manage all the aspects of your course –
communication, information distribution, testing and grading.

Let it help you:

- **Communicate directly with your students** via email, discussion boards, and announcement pages.

- **Post documents for your course,** eliminating the need for course packs or handouts.

- **Administer online tests,** with automatic grading and analysis.

- **Provide your students with 24/7 access** to key course information, such as syllabus, assignments, and additional resources – as well as check his/her grade instantly.

Demo CourseCompass today! www.coursecompass.com

Instructor's Manual

for

Pinel

Biopsychology

Fifth Edition

prepared by

Michael J. Mana
Western Washington University

Boston   New York   San Francisco
Mexico City   Montreal   Toronto   London   Madrid   Munich   Paris
Hong Kong   Singapore   Tokyo   Cape Town   Sydney

ISBN 0-205-37328-3

Printed in the United States of America

10 9 8 7 6 5 4 3 2 1   08 07 06 05 04 03 02

Table of Contents

PREFACE

HOW TO USE THIS INSTRUCTOR'S MANUAL

I hope that the lecture notes contained in this Instructor's Manual prove useful in your presentation of the material from the 5th Edition of **BIOPSYCHOLOGY.** Each chapter in the text is represented by 2 or 3 lectures that capture the key points of the chapter. To make them truly effective, I urge you to use the lecture notes presented in this Instructor's Manual as a skeleton for your own set of notes…but make the clothes your own by adding your own anecdotes, personal experiences, research interests and biopsychology trivia. To this end, you can obtain all of the files for the lectures in this Instructor's Manual simply by contacting me at *MIKE.MANA@WWU.EDU.*

INTEGRATION WITH OTHER *BIOPSYCHOLOGY* ANCILLARIES.

The lecture notes for each chapter are prefaced by a **Chapter-At-A-Glance grid** that integrates the lecture notes with four other valuable resources that accompany *BIOPSYCHOLOGY:*

1) BIOPSYCHOLOGY: BEYOND BRAIN & BEHAVIOR CD-ROM. Included with each copy of **BIOPSYCHOLOGY,** this CD contains a collection of teaching aids to assist you and your students. These include a series of *QuickTime movies* that illustrate key points in the text; *Practice Tests* for your students; a *Hard Copy* section that will help your students learn more about different topics covered in that chapter; and *Electronic Flashcards* to help your students learn the material more efficiently.

2) DIGITAL IMAGE ARCHIVE CD-ROM FOR BIOPSYCHOLOGY. This CD is available upon request from your Allyn and Bacon representative. To find the figures on the CD-ROM, look in Pinel/Images/BMP for a directory containing images from each chapter. Note that the numbering of the figures in the fifth edition of **BIOPSYCHOLOGY** do not match with the indexing for the figures on the CD-ROM; to make your life easier, the lecture notes in the Instructor's Manual refer to the appropriate file name from the CD-ROM. If you are blessed with a multi-media classroom, you can display the figures directly from the CD-ROM; if you are using more conventional teaching resources, you can print the figures from the *Digital Image Archive* onto overheads. This CD is available upon request from your Allyn and Bacon representative.

3) BIOLOGICAL PSYCHOLOGY Video. Allyn and Bacon's *Video for Biological Psychology* contains short video segments garnered from Films for the Humanities and Sciences. Each video segments cover such topics as: anatomy of the brain, DNA, genetics, neurotransmitters, how drugs influence electric impulses in the brain, methods of studying the brain, brain damage, the senses, eating, hormones, sleep, drug addiction, memory, and neuroplasticity. The video segments will help students better understand the workings of the brain and will foster classroom discussion. This video is available upon request from your Allyn and Bacon representative.

4) TRANSPARENCIES FOR PHYSIOLOGICAL PSYCHOLOGY. These transparencies include artwork from **BIOPSYCHOLOGY** that will complement your lectures and help you to illustrate key concepts from the text. They are available upon request from your Allyn and Bacon representative.

If you have any comments about the Instructor's Manual or any of **BIOPSYCHOLOGY'S** other ancillaries, feel free to contact me at MIKE.MANA@WWU.EDU. Otherwise, I hope that you and your students enjoy **BIOPSYCHOLOGY.** All the best…

Open-Book Testing: Why It Makes Sense

By Kay Burke, Ph.D.

Educators who allow students to take open-book tests are not teaching *for the test*; they are teaching *for understanding*. Most students agree that open-book tests are more challenging than traditional objective tests because they require high-order thinking skills rather than recall skills.

The greatest benefit from open-book testing may be that it encourages the type of thinking that will benefit students in the real world.

- Open-book tests focus on students learning important concepts rather than memorizing facts.

- They encourage students to utilize the lifelong learning skill of "accessing information" rather than memorizing data. In most jobs, people do not have to memorize formulas or discrete bits of data; they have to know how to find the important information they need in order to solve problems and complete projects.

- Open-book tests encourage students to highlight the text and organize their notes so they can find the information they need.

- Open-book tests encourage students to **apply** the information they have learned and **transfer** it to new situations, rather than just repeat the facts.

Sources:

Burke, K.B. *The Mindful School: How to Assess Authentic Learning*. Arlington Heights, IL. Skylight Professional Development

Stiggins, R.J. (1985, October). Improving Assessment where it Means the Most: In the Classroom. *Educational Leadership*, pp. 69-74.

Wiggins, G. (1989, April). Creating tests worth taking. *Educational Leadership*, pp. 121-127

Wiggins, G. and McTighe, J. (1989). *Understanding by Design*. Alexandria, VA: Association for Supervision and Curriculum Development

IM-At-A-Glance. Chapter 1: Biopsychology as a Neuroscience: What is Biopsychology, Anyway?

Detailed Outline	Print Supplements	Media Supplements	Professor's Notes
Chapter 1. Biopsychology as a Neuroscience: What is Biopsychology, Anyway? pp. 1-18 *1.1 What is Biopsychology?* *1.2 What Is The Relation Between Biopsychology and the Other Disciplines of Neuroscience?* *1.3 What Types of Research Characterize the Biopsychological Approach?* *1.4 What Are the Divisions of Biopsychology?* *1.5 Converging Operations: How Do Biopsychologists Work Together?* *1.6 Scientific Inference: How Do Biopsychologists Study the Unobservable Workings of the Brain?* *1.7 Critical Thinking About Biopsychological Claims*	**Instructor's Manual for** ***BIOPSYCHOLOGY,*** *Lecture 1a and Lecture 1b* **Test Bank for** ***BIOPSYCHOLOGY,*** *Chapter 1* **Study Guide for** ***BIOPSYCHOLOGY,*** *Chapter 1* **Transparencies for Physiological Psychology:** *I. An Introduction to the Study of Brain & Behavior*	**Beyond the Brain & Behavior CD for** ***BIOPSYCHOLOGY:*** *Themes of Biopsychology module; Perception of Motion module* *Practice Tests for Chapter 1* *Hard Copy for Chapter 1* *Electronic Flashcards for Chapter 1* **Digital Image Archive, Powerpoint Presentation and Bitmap Images for** ***BIOPSYCHOLOGY:*** *Chapter 1*	

Lecture 1a

BIOPSYCHOLOGY AS A NEUROSCIENCE:
What is Biopsychology, Anyway?

Outline

1. **A Personal Introduction**

    a. Describe your training and teaching experiences
    b. Describe your research interests
    c. Introduce your teaching assistant(s)
    d. Discuss your (and your teaching assistant's) availability: Office Location; Hours; E-Mail address; Web page

2. **The Organization of The Course**

    a. Who Is The Course For?
    b. Text and Ancillary Materials
    c. Lecture Format
    d. Examination Format
    e. Major Assignments
    f. Special Learning Requirements
    g. Missed Exams/Assignments Policy
    h. Final Grades

3. **What is Biopsychology?**

    a. Study of biological bases of behavior
    b. Characterized by an eclectic approach

4. **Biopsychology as a Discipline of Neuroscience**

    a. What is Neuroscience?
    b. Biopsychology as a part of Neuroscience

5. **The Diversity of Biopsychological Research**

    a. Human and Nonhuman Subjects
    b. Experiments and Nonexperiments
    c. Pure and Applied Research

Lecture Notes

1. **A Personal Introduction...**

    -   in order to lend this course a personal perspective, let me tell you a bit about myself.

    a. **Training and Teaching Experience**

        -   how I first became interested in biopsychology (personal anecdote)
        -   undergraduate training
        -   graduate training
        -   postgraduate experience
        -   courses currently teaching

b.   Research Experience

- thesis research
- past research
- current research interests

The following information should also be included in the syllabus that you handed out…

c.   Teaching Assistant (if possible, have the TA speak about him/her self)

- training; current research interests

d.   Availability of Instructor and Teaching Assistant

- office hours and location
- phone numbers/e-mail addresses/web pages

2.   Organization of The Course…What You and I Can Expect!

a.   Who is The Course For?

- describe any prerequisites for the course (e.g., Introductory Psychology; Introductory Biology)

b.   Text and Ancillary Materials (bring these to class so the students can see them)

- *BIOPSYCHOLOGY, 5th Edition*, by John P.J. Pinel
- *STUDY GUIDE for BIOPSYCHOLOGY, 5th Edition*, by Michael J. Mana
- *BEYOND THE BRAIN & BEHAVIOR CD-ROM* to accompany *BIOPSYCHOLOGY, 5th Edition*
- other assigned reading material

c.   Lecture Format

- relation of lectures to text
- each lecture will begin with an outline
- questions or comments are encouraged throughout the lecture

d.   Examination Format

- examination dates and content
- nature of final exam (comprehensive or for last block of material?)
- nature of questions…multiple choice and/or short answer and/or essay and/or figure identification
- how grades will be reported; grade cutoffs
- what to do if you think your examination has been incorrectly graded

e.   Major Assignments

- what are they; when are they due?

f.   Special Learning or Examination Requirements

- provide information about your institution's learning resource center

g.   Missed Examination or Assignment Policy

h.   Final Grades

- how the final grades will be computed

3. What is Biopsychology?

a. Study of biological bases of behavior

- **brain** and **behavior** are two of the most interesting subjects of scientific research; **biopsychology** focuses on the relation between them
- biopsychology began to emerge as a distinct area in psychology towards the end of the 19th century; many psychologists point to Hebb's *The Organization of Behavior* (1949) as a key factor in its development into a major neuroscientific discipline
- biopsychologists study how the brain and the rest of the nervous system determine what we perceive, feel, think, say, and do
- this may prove to be the *ultimate challenge for the human brain*…does our brain have the capacity to understand something as complex as itself?

b. Characterized by an eclectic approach

- a biopsychologist uses an **eclectic** combination of theories and research from many different areas (e.g., psychology, biology, physiology, pharmacology and anatomy) to better describe, understand and predict behavior
- this diverse approach is captured by the 4 main themes of *BIOPSYCHOLOGY:* **critical thought** about biopsychology; the **clinical implications** of biopsychology; **evolution** and biopsychology; and **cognitive neuroscience** and biopsychology

4. Biopsychology as a Discipline of Neuroscience

a. What is Neuroscience?

- until the middle of the last century, the brain was studied primarily by philosophers; since then, it has been subjected more and more to scientific study
- **neuroscience** is the study of the nervous system; neuroscience includes many different approaches including **neuroanatomy, neurophysiology, neurochemistry, neuroendocrinology, neuropharmacology,** and **neuropathology**

b. Biopsychology as a part of Neuroscience

- **biopsychology** is the discipline of neuroscience that integrates these various approaches to the study of the nervous system; biopsychologists try to discover how the various phenomena studied by neurophysiologists, neuropharmacologists, neuroanatomists and other neuroscience researchers relate to one another to produce psychological phenomena such as learning, memory, motivation, and perception
- thus, biopsychology can be viewed as **bridge** between the disciplines of psychology and neuroscience
- the first part of the course will examine the fundamentals of neuroanatomy, neurophysiology, neuropharmacology, genetics, and evolution; the rest of the course will focus on how these biological fundamentals are applied to the study of biopsychological phenomena

5. The Diversity of Biopsychological Research

- biopsychologists use a variety of research approaches in their studies; to understand what biopsychology is, you must understand what biopsychologists do
- this diversity can be illustrated by discussing three dimensions along which biopsychological research varies:

    a) **human vs. nonhuman subjects**   b) experimental vs. nonexperimental studies

    c) applied vs. pure research

a. Human and Nonhuman Subjects

Advantages of human subjects:
- they can follow directions
- they can report subjective experiences
- they are often less expensive
- they have a human brain

Advantages of nonhuman subjects:
- they have simpler nervous systems
- studying various species makes it possible to use the **comparative approach**
- there are fewer ethical constraints (although the ethics of both human and animal research is carefully scrutinized by independent committees)

b. Experiments and Nonexperiments

- biopsychological research can involve **experiments** and **nonexperimental studies** (quasiexperimental designs and case studies)

Experiments (see Fig. 1.3 in *BIOPSYCHOLOGY*)

- the experiment is the method used by scientists to determine **cause-and-effect relationships**
- usually a different group of subjects is tested under each treatment condition of the experiment; this is a **between-subjects design**
- sometimes the same group of subjects can be tested under multiple treatment conditions; this is a **within-subjects design**
- **Independent Variables:** are set or manipulated by the experimenter; these manipulations produce the different treatment conditions in an experiment
- **Dependent Variables:** reflect the subject's behavior; this is what the experimenter measures
- the experimenter tries to conduct the experiment in such a way that the independent variable is the only thing that varies between each treatment condition; the experimenter measures the effect of the independent variable on the dependent variable
- in a well-designed experiment, the experimenter can conclude that any differences in the dependent variable between the various treatment conditions were *caused* by the independent variable (it's the only possibility)
- although the principle of good experimentation is conceptually simple, it is often difficult in practice to make sure that there is only one difference among conditions; other unintended differences among conditions that can influence the dependent variable are called *confounded variables*
- the presence of confounded variables makes experiments difficult to interpret because it is impossible to tell how much (if any) of the effect on the dependent variable was caused by the independent variable and how much (if any) was caused by the confounded variable
- an example of a well-designed experiment is the experiment of Lester and Gorzalka (1988) on the **Coolidge effect** in female hamsters

Nonexperimental Studies

- sometimes it is impossible to conduct controlled experiments; e.g., if human subjects are involved, it may be impossible for ethical or technical reasons to assign them to particular conditions and to administer the conditions.
- in a **quasiexperimental design,** researchers examine subjects in real world situations who have self-selected into specific conditions (e.g., excessive alcohol intake); in a sense, these subjects have assigned themselves to treatment conditions
- the major shortcoming of a quasiexperimental study is that although researchers can examine relations between the variables of interest (e.g., alcohol consumption's relation to brain damage), a quasiexperimental study cannot control for potential confounding variables and therefore does not allow a researcher to establish direct cause-and-effect relationships

Example: researchers cannot randomly assign humans to Control and Alcohol groups, and then expose one group to 10 years of chronic alcohol exposure to see if alcohol causes brain damage; instead, they must compare the brains of alcoholics and nonalcoholics found in the real world. This is a classic quasiexperimental study.

Key Problem: because subjects in the real world do not assign themselves to groups randomly, there are many other differences among the groups that could contribute to differences in the dependent measures. For example, the observation that alcoholics have far more brain damage than nonalcoholics does NOT mean that alcohol directly causes this difference because alcoholics differ from nonalcoholics in many ways unrelated to their alcohol consumption (e.g., education; accidental head injury; diet; other drug use).

-   another type of nonexperimental design is called a **case study**
-   case studies are scientific studies that focus on a **single subject**; for example, you will learn later in the course about how the in-depth study of one amnesic subject (H.M.) has contributed much to our understanding of the neural basis of memory
-   the main problem with case studies is their **generalizability,** or the extent to which their results tell us something about the general population

A Key Point: Experiments, quasiexperimental studies, and case studies can all make valuable scientific contributions, particularly when they are used to complement one another (e.g., they have all contributed to our understanding of the relation between alcohol consumption and brain damage)

c.   **Pure and Applied Research**

-   pure and applied research are defined by the motivation of the researcher
-   **pure research** is motivated primarily by the curiosity of the researcher; it is motivated by the desire to find out how things work; pure research focuses on establishing building blocks or basic concepts that may provide information salient to many problems.
-   **applied research** is motivated by an attempt to directly use the building blocks of basic research to answer specific questions; human and animal problems are directly addressed

Closing Comments:

-   biopsychologists study the biology of behavior in a variety of ways; the strength of biopsychology as a science is attributable to this diversity; its diversity also makes biopsychology an exciting and challenging field of study

Suggested Web Resources for Lecture 1a:

Biopsychology and the Nobel Prize: *http://faculty.washington.edu/chudler/nobel.html*
List of Nobel Prize winners from the behavioral and brain sciences.

A Timeline of Neuroscience: *http://neurolab.jsc.nasa.gov/timeline.htm*
From NASA's Neurolab, a time-line on the history of neuroscience.

The Society for Neuroscience: *http://www.sfn.org*
Homepage for the Society for Neuroscience.

The American Psychological Association: *http://www.apa.org*
Homepage for the APA.

The American Psychological Society: *http://www.psychologicalscience.org*
Homepage for the APS.

The concepts of science, in all their richness and ambiguity,
can be presented without any compromise...
in language accessible to all intelligent people.

Stephen Jay Gould

Lecture 1b

BIOPSYCHOLOGICAL RESEARCH

Outline

1. **Summary of Preceding Lecture**

2. **The Six Divisions of Biopsychology**

    a. Physiological Psychology
    b. Psychopharmacology
    c. Neuropsychology
    d. Psychophysiology
    e. Cognitive Neuroscience
    f. Comparative Psychology

3. **Converging Operations: How Do Biopsychologists Work Together?**

    - biopsychological research integrates information from several different approaches

4. **Scientific Inference: How Biopsychologists Study the Unobservable**

    - the scientific method and scientific inference

5. **Critical Thinking and Biopsychology: Two Examples of BS (Bad Science)**

    a. Taming a Charging Bull with Brain Stimulation
    b. Prefrontal Lobotomy

6. **Class Discussion**

    a. What was wrong with Delgado's claims?
    b. What was wrong with Moniz's claims?

Lecture Notes

1. **Brief Summary of Preceding Lecture**

    -   biopsychology is a part of neuroscience
    -   biopsychological research is diverse:
        -   human and nonhuman subjects
        -   experiments, quasiexperimental studies, and case studies
        -   pure and applied research

2. The Six Divisions of Biopsychology (see Fig. 1.5 in *BIOPSYCHOLOGY;* use *Digital Image Archive CHO1F06.BMP)*

    a. **Physiological Psychology**

        -   focuses on **direct manipulation** of the nervous system in controlled laboratory settings (e.g., lesions, electrical stimulation, invasive recording)
        -   thus, the subjects are usually laboratory animals
        -   strong focus on **pure research**

b. **Psychopharmacology**

- similar to physiological psychology except that the nervous system is manipulated pharmacologically
- focuses on drug effects on behavior and how these changes are mediated by changes in neural activity
- many psychopharmacologists favor **pure research** and use drugs to reveal the nature of brain-behavior interactions; many others study **applied questions** (e.g., drug abuse, therapeutic drugs)

c. **Neuropsychology**

- focuses on the behavioral deficits produced in **humans** by brain damage, typically **cortical damage**
- can't be studied in humans by experimentation; deals almost exclusively with **case studies** and **quasiexperimental studies**
- most applied of the six divisions of biopsychology; neuropsychological tests of brain-damaged patients facilitate diagnosis, treatment, and lifestyle counseling (e.g., the case of Mr. R described in the text)

d. **Psychophysiology**

- focuses on the relation between physiology and behavior by recording the physiological responses of human subjects
- because human subjects are used, all brain recording is **noninvasive** (i.e., from the surface of the head)
- usual measure of brain activity is the **scalp electroencephalogram (EEG)**
- muscle tension, eye movement, heart rate, pupil dilation, and electrical conductance of the skin are other common psychophysiological measures

e. **Cognitive Neuroscience**

- newest division of biopsychology
- focuses on the **neural bases of cognitive processes** like learning and memory, attention, and complex perceptual processes
- often employs human subjects; key methods are **noninvasive, functional brain imaging techniques**
- often involves collaborations between researchers with widely different backgrounds (e.g., biopsychology, cognitive psychology, computer science)

f. **Comparative Psychology**

- study of **evolutionary and genetic factors** in behavior
- features **comparative** and **functional** approaches
- features laboratory research as well as studies of animals in their natural environments **(ethology)**

3. **Converging Operations: How Do Biopsychologists Work Together?**

- the methods of the six divisions of biopsychology are not without their weaknesses; thus, biopsychological issues are rarely resolved by a single experiment or study, or by a single approach
- progress is greatest when several different approaches, each compensating for the shortcomings of the others, are used to solve the same problems; this is called *converging operations*

Example: Consider the relative strengths and weakness of **physiological psychology** and **neuropsychology.** Neuropsychology's strength is that it deals with humans, but this is also its weakness because it precludes experimentation. In contrast, physiological psychology can bring the power of the experimental method and invasive neuroscientific techniques to bear on the question, but it is limited to the study of laboratory animals.

Because the two approaches complement one another, together they can provide evidence for points of view that neither can defend individually. Read about the case of Jimmie G. in Section 1.5 to see the power of this approach in action!

4. **Scientific Inference: How Biopsychologists Study the Unobservable**

- science is a method of answering questions by direct observation; it is an **empirical method**
- however, brain activity is not directly observable (e.g., one can't see a neuron firing or neurochemicals being released from neurons)
- this situation is no different than that in the other sciences; e.g., physicists cannot see gravity, chemists cannot see evaporation; the effects of these processes are observable but not the processes themselves

> **Question:** *How do scientists study the unobservable by a method (i.e., the scientific method) that is fundamentally observational?*

> **Answer:** *By **scientific inference**; scientists observe the consequences of unobservable processes and from these they infer the nature of unobservable processes.*

> **Example: Eye Movement Example** (see Fig. 1.6 from *BIOPSYCHOLOGY*)

- manually move your eye upward; the world appears to move downward. This is because the brain interprets movement across the retina as movement of the world unless the eye movements are actively produced by the brain itself

> (**Note:** Use the *Perception of Motion* module on the ***BEYOND THE BRAIN & BEHAVIOR CD-ROM*** that accompanies Biopsychology to demonstrate how the brain perceives motion).

5. **Critical Thinking and Biopsychology: Two Examples of BS (Bad Science)** (see Fig. 1.7 from *BIOPSYCHOLOGY*; use *Digital Image Archive, Chpt 1, CH01F08.BMP; CH01F09.BMP; and CH01F10.BMP*)

- you might think it odd to begin a course on biopsychology by considering two bad examples of its science; this is done for two reasons:

1) because disciplines learn from their mistakes, understanding biopsychology's previous errors provides insights into what it is today; and

2) because it will make you a better consumer of scientific research--it will help you develop **critical thinking** about biopsychological research.

a. **Taming a Charging Bull with Caudate Stimulation**

- the biopsychologist Jose Delgado implanted an **electrode** into the **caudate nucleus** of a bull
- each time the bull charged, Delgado delivered a stimulation to its caudate nucleus through the implanted electrode by activating a hand-held radio transmitter
- this stopped the charge; after a few attempts the bull stood tamely as Delgado strode about the ring
- Delgado and the popular press declared this a major discovery, the discovery of the caudate **taming center.** It was even suggested that caudate stimulation might cure human psychopaths.

b. **Prefrontal Lobotomy**

- in 1949, Dr. Egas Moniz was awarded a Nobel prize for developing a treatment for mental illness: **prefrontal lobotomy,** a form of neurosurgery that cuts the connections between the prefrontal lobes and the rest of the brain
- Moniz based his technique on a report that a **chimpanzee** (Becky) was easier to handle after part of her prefrontal lobes had been destroyed in an experiment
- following the initial reports by Moniz of the operation's beneficial effects, it was performed on mentally ill patients all over the world (over 40,000 in the U.S.A. alone)
- various forms of the operation were devised such as the **transorbital lobotomy** procedure, which was performed by inserting an icepick-like device through the eye sockets, often in the doctor's office

6. Class Discussion

-   guide the discussion to the following points and issues

a. What was wrong with Delgado's claims?

-   there are many ways that stimulation might stop a charging bull other than by taming it (e.g., the stimulation might have been painful, blinded the bull, made it sick, or made movement difficult)
-   when there is more than one reasonable interpretation of a behavior, the general rule is to favor the most simple one; this rule is called **Morgan's Canon** (similar to **Occam's Razor**)
-   in fact, analyses of the filmed record of this event strongly support a more simple interpretation: the left and right caudate are motor structures and stimulating one side often causes an animal to walk in circles. This appears to be what happened here; the bull was left confused and incapable of charging, but not tamed.

Questions for Class:

1) *Why do you think that an experienced scientist like Delgado would stage events like this for the popular press and exaggerate their significance?*
2) *Why do you think the popular press and general public were so gullible?*

b. What was wrong with Moniz's claims?

-   the surgery was based on the study of only one subject (Becky), and a nonhuman subject at that!
-   it is difficult to see how one could conclude that an operation that would eliminate the adaptive defensive reactions of a chimpanzee to an experimenter would help the mentally ill
-   Moniz and others who prescribed prefrontal lobotomy were not in a position to be objective in its evaluation, nor were they trained to perform such evaluation studies. Early reports of the benefits of prefrontal lobotomy were based on poorly controlled studies that focused on **manageability** and were published by Moniz himself.
-   after many thousands of people had been lobotomized, controlled studies by objective researchers revealed terrible side effects, e.g., "vegetable-like behavior", urinary incontinence, epilepsy

Questions for Class:

1) *Moniz was a physician, not a researcher: What were the repercussions of this?*
2) *To what extent do you think that Moniz's claims were widely accepted by other physicians because they had no research training? To what extent do you think that Moniz's claims were widely accepted because there were no effective ways of treating mental illness at the time?*
3) *Could such a travesty happen today?*

Suggested Web Resources for Lecture 1b:

Moniz and The Prefrontal Lobotomy: *http://www.pbs.org/wgbh/aso/databank/entries/dh35lo.html*
    From WGBH Boston and the Public Broadcasting Service (PBS), a page about Moniz and the prefrontal lobotomy.

A History of Psychosurgery: *http://www.epub.org.br/cm/n02/historia/psicocirg_i.htm*
    From the Brain and Mind website at the State University of Campinas in Brazil, an easy-to-read history of psychosurgery. See also:

Psychosurgery: *http://neurosurgery.mgh.harvard.edu/psysurg.htm*
    A text-only site about psychosurgery, both historically and in the modern-day; moderately difficult but very informative.

IM-At-A-Glance. Chapter 2: Evolution, Genetics & Experience: Thinking About the Biology of Behavior

Detailed Outline	Print Supplements	Media Supplements	Professor's Notes
Chapter 2. Evolution, Genetics & Experience: Thinking About the Biology of Behavior, pp. 19-50	**Instructor's Manual for** *BIOPSYCHOLOGY,* *Lecture 2a and* *Lecture 2b*	***Beyond the Brain & Behavior CD for* BIOPSYCHOLOGY:** *Practice Tests for Chapter 2*	
2.1 Thinking About the Biology of Behavior	**Test Bank for** *BIOPSYCHOLOGY,* *Chapter 2*	*Hard Copy for Chapter 2*	
2.2 Human Evolution		*Electronic Flashcards for Chapter 2*	
2.3 Fundamental Genetics	**Study Guide for** *BIOPSYCHOLOGY,* *Chapter 2*	**Digital Image Archive, Powerpoint Presentation and Bitmap Images for** *BIOPSYCHOLOGY:* *Chapter 2*	
2.4 Behavioral Development			
2.5 The Genetics of Human Psychological Differences		**BIOLOGICAL PSYCHOLOGY VIDEO:** *Segment 2. The Transmission of Genes*	

Lecture 2a

EVOLUTION AND GENETICS

Outline

1. Darwin's Theory of Evolution

2. Behavior and Evolution
   a. Social dominance
   b. Courtship displays

3. Human Evolution
   a. Course of Human Evolution
   b. Thinking About Human Evolution
   c. Evolution of the Human Brain
   d. Evolutionary Psychology

4. Fundamental Genetics
   a. Mendelian Genetics
   b. Chromosomes, Reproduction and Sex-Linked Traits
   c. Chromosome Structure, Replication and Gene Expression

5. Human Genome Project

Lecture Notes

1. Darwin's Theory of Evolution

- Darwin (1859) publishes *ON THE ORIGINS OF THE SPECIES* and modern biology is born
- Darwin's theory that species **evolve** (undergo gradual orderly change) is the most influential in the biological sciences
- Darwin was not the first to propose this idea, but he was the first to provide strong evidence for it from: 1) **fossil records;** 2) **structural similarities** among existing species; and 3) programs of **selective breeding**
- even stronger evidence comes from modern genetic studies and from observations of evolution in progress; e.g., Grant's (1991) study of changes in Galápagos finches after a 1-year drought--beak size increased in response to shortage of small seeds
- Darwin was also the first to suggest the mechanism by which evolution takes place: **natural selection,** in which normal variations in a characteristic that are associated with increased **fitness** (high rates of survival and reproduction) are most likely to be passed on to future generations
- the evidence for the theory of evolution is unassailable; it meets with no significant opposition from the biological community

2. Evolution and Behavior

- early studies of evolution focused on structure; **behavior** also plays an important role in determining an organism's fitness
- the contributions of some behaviors (e.g., eating, sexual behavior, predatory behavior) are obvious; others are less obvious but no less important; two examples are **social aggression** and **courtship displays**

a. Social Dominance

- males of many species establish hierarchies of social dominance by combative encounters with other males
- social dominance influences evolution because dominant males (or females, in some species) are able to copulate more. **Example:** in a study of bull elephant seals McCann (1981) found that the highest ranking bull accounted for 37% of copulations; the lowest ranking bull accounted for only 1%

a. **Courtship Displays**

- courtship displays precede copulation in many species
- copulation is unlikely if one partner fails to respond appropriately to the displays of the other
- courtship displays are important to evolution because they can promote the formation of new species; the evolution of an idiosyncratic courtship display can form a **reproductive barrier** that is as effective as geographic separation

3. **Human Evolution** (see Figure 2.10 and Fig. 2.11 in *BIOPSYCHOLOGY;* use *Digital Image Archive, Chpt 2. CH02F03.BMP)*

a. **Course of Human Evolution**

- about 600 million years ago the first multi-cell organisms evolved in the oceans
- about 450 million years ago, the first **chordates** (animals with dorsal nerve cords) evolved
- 425 million years ago, the first chordates with backbones (i.e., **vertebrates**) evolved; they were bony fishes
- 410 million years ago, bony fishes first ventured onto land to escape stagnant pools and take advantage of untapped food sources; the Florida walking catfish is a survivor of this stage
- 400 million years ago, the first amphibians evolved; they are born in water and spend their larval stage there, but as adults they have legs and lungs and can survive on land
- 300 million years ago the first **reptiles** evolved from amphibians; they spend the first stage of their lives in the watery environment of a shell-covered egg; dry scales reduce water loss and allow adults to live away from water.
- 180 million years ago, during the age of dinosaurs, a line of reptiles evolved that fed their young through **mammary glands**; eventually, **mammals** stopped laying eggs and nurtured their young in the watery environment of their bodies
- today, there are 14 different orders of mammals; the one we belong to is **primates;** there are five different families of primates: **prosimians, old-world monkeys, new-world monkeys, apes**, and **hominids**
- the hominid family is composed of two genera: **Homo** and **Australopithecus**
- 6 million years ago, Australopithecus is thought to have evolved from a species of African apes
- Australopithecines were 1.3 meters (4 feet) tall, they had small brains, they had an upright walk, and they became extinct about 1 million years ago
- 2 million years ago the first Homo species evolved from Australopithecus; these hominids used tools and fire, but had a relatively small brain
- 200,000 years ago, modern humans **(homo sapiens)** evolved

> *Interesting Point:* Though the human attributes of a big brain, upright posture, and free hands evolved hundreds of thousands of years ago, most uniquely human accomplishments occurred only within the last 25,000 years...

b. **Thinking About Human Evolution**

When thinking about human evolution, keep the following 8 points in mind:

1) Evolution does not proceed in a straight line.
2) Homo sapiens do NOT represent evolutionary supremacy.
3) Evolution is not always a slow, gradual process.
4) Present species represent a fraction of the species that have evolved on earth.
5) Evolution is not a perfectionist.
6) Evolution is not always adaptive; nonadaptive evolutionary byproducts are called **spandrels.**
7) Sometimes structures or behaviors evolve in response to one type of evolutionary pressure, but later perform a different function; these types of changes are called **expatations.**
8) Similarities between species does not mean a common evolutionary origin: keep in mind the differences between homologous structures (with a common evolutionary origin) and **analogous structures** (with different but convergent evolutionary processes in their origins)

c. **Evolution of the Human Brain**

- size is not the key to the intellectual power of the human brain; there is no relationship between size and intellectual capacity in humans, and human beings do not have the largest brains in the animal kingdom

- 3 key points about the evolution of the human brain:

  i) it has **increased in size** during the course of evolution.
  ii) most of this increase in size has occurred in the **cerebrum.**
  iii) the increased size of the cerebrum has been accompanied by increased **convolutions** of the cortex.

- the similarities between the brains of different species is more significant that the differences between them. All brains are composed of neurons, these neurons generally function in a similar fashion, and in most cases similar structures can be found between species.

d. **Evolutionary Psychology: Understanding Mate Bonding**

- **evolutionary psychology** seeks to understand human behaviors by considering the pressures that led to their evolution; much attention has focused on the issue of **mate bonding** (enduring mating relationships)
- in mammals, this may be due to fact that there are relatively few young which are helpless and slow to develop. Thus, it is adaptive for males to stay with females and promote the success of their young...and it is adaptive for females to evolve behaviors that will promote this type of bonding.
- **polygyny** (male bonds with multiple females) is the most common form of mate bonding. The males of most species contribute little more than sperm to the development of the young; the investment of the female is much more substantial. Thus, in many species the females evolved strategies to promote bonding with the most dominant males (to increase the likelihood their young will survive) whereas males mate form bonds with as many females as possible (resulting in polygyny).
- when the male's contribution to reproduction outweighs the females, **polyandry** (female mates with multiple males) has evolved (**Example:** in seahorse species, where the males tend to the eggs and the young until they are mature enough to survive on their own.)
- when the survival of offspring is enhanced if the males helps to raise the young, **monogamy** (a single male bonds with a single female) has evolved as the optimal reproductive strategy
- developments in evolutionary psychology emphasize 3 key points: 1) evolutionary analyses can be applied to the most complex human behaviors; 2) humans are the product of evolution; and 3) humans are closely related to other animals species

4. **Fundamental Genetics** (see Figure 2.13, Fig 2.15 - Fig. 2.17 in *BIOPSYCHOLOGY*; use *Digital Image Archive, Chpt 2. CH02F13.BMP, CH02F15.BMP, CH02F16.BMP, CH02F17.BMP; CH02F19.BMP;* and *CH02F20.BMP)*

a. **Mendelian Genetics**
- Darwin did not understand how structural or behavioral traits could be passed from generation to generation, or how conspecifics could differ from one another. These processes were first documented by **Gregor Mendel,** an Augustinian monk.
- the key to Mendel's success is that he studied **dichotomous traits** (characteristics that occur in one form or another, never a mix; Mendel studied the inheritance of the color of peas) and **true-breeding lines** (in which interbred members always produce offspring with the same trait)
- **KEY FINDING:** when true-bred brown and white peas are crossed, the offspring of first crosses ALL had brown seeds whereas 25% of the offspring of second crosses had white seeds; this disproved the prevalent view that offspring inherit their parents' exhibited traits
- Mendel proposed each dichotomous trait was due to two kinds of inherited factors: these are called **genes.** Furthermore, each individual contains two genes for each dichotomous trait; these are called **alleles**

- these results led to Mendel's development of the concepts of:
    i. **dominant traits** (appear in 100% of first crosses) and **recessive traits** (appear in about 25% of second crosses)
    ii. **genotype** (genetic traits passed on to offspring) and **phenotype** (observable genetic traits)
    iii. **homozygous** organisms (that possess identical genes for a trait) and **heterozygous** organisms (that possess different genes for a trait)

b. Chromosomes, Reproduction and Sex-Linked Traits

- in early 1900's genes were localized to paired thread-like structures in the cell nucleus called **chromosomes**
- **gametes** (eggs and sperm cells) are produced when cells divide during **meiosis**. One chromosome from each chromosome pair in the parent cell goes to each of two gametes produced when that cell divides; thus, each gamete has half the usual number of chromosomes. When they combine during fertilization the resulting **zygote** has the normal number of chromosomes (half from each parent).
- the strongest early evidence of this came from studies of **linkage** between various traits in a species (such that individuals expressing one trait usually expressed several other *linked traits*). In each species, the number of clusters of linked traits equals the number of pairs of chromosomes, suggesting that the traits were *linked* by their presence on the same chromosome.
- **crossing over** explains why traits on a chromosome are not always linked (i.e., inherited together); crossing over is important because it allows increases species diversity
- **Sex Chromosomes:** are not found in matched pairs. Females have 2 X chromosomes; males have an X and a Y chromosome. **Sex-linked traits** are traits associated with the sex chromosomes, usually the X chromosome as Ychromosomes carries few genes other than those that cause a zygote to develop into a male.

c. Chromosome Structure, Replication & Gene Expression

- each chromosome is a double-stranded molecule of **deoxyribonucleic acid (DNA),** made of one of 4 nucleotide bases: **adenine, thymine, guanine,** and **cytosine.** The sequence of these bases on each chromosome constitutes the genetic code
- each strand of DNA is the **complement** of the other, as thymine is attracted to adenine and guanine is attracted to cytosine. During **replication,** as the strands of DNA unwind each base in a strand attracts its complement so that when unwinding is complete two new strands of DNA are created.
- **operator genes** control the ability of **structural genes** to initiate the synthesis of specific single proteins. Often, operator genes are regulated by **DNA-binding proteins** that are influenced by environmental factors; this is the way that experience interacts with genes to influence development.

5. Human Genome Project

- perhaps the most ambitious scientific project of all time; has mapped the base sequence of each of the 200,000 genes located on the 46 chromosomes that human beings possess
- a greater task will be to identify the millions of variations that can occur in human genes and to understand how these variations and the environment influence human structure and function
- eventually, the knowledge will be used to better understand and treat genetically-based diseases (e.g., by substituting healthy genes for flawed ones) and to better understand the genetic bases of behavior

Suggested Web Resources for Lecture 2a

Charles Darwin: *http://www.brunette.brucity.be/PEGASE/darwin/endarwin.htm*
From BRUNETTE, an extensive biography of Charles Darwin and the development of his theory of evolution.

Evolution and the Brain: *http://brainmuseum.org/*
From the University of Wisconsin, a site on the evolution of the brain, complete with downloadable images of brains across the phylogenetic tree.

The Human Genome Project: *http://www.ornl.gov/TechResources/Human_Genome/home.html*
Website of the Human Genome project, sponsored by the US Dept of Energy.

Lecture 2b

**THINKING ABOUT THE
BIOLOGY OF BEHAVIOR**

Outline

1.   Thinking in Dichotomies

2.   Current Thinking About the Biology of Behavior
     a. Physiological or Psychological?
     b. Inherited or Learned?
     c. A 6-Stage Model of the Biology of Behavior

3.   Behavioral Development: The Interaction of Genetic Factors and Experience
     a. Selective Breeding of "Maze-Bright" and "Maze-Dull" Rats
     b. Phenylketonuria: A Single-Gene Metabolic Disorder
     c. Development of Bird Song

4.   The Genetics of Human Psychological Differences

Lecture Notes

1.   Thinking in Dichotomies

-   we tend to think about behavior in terms of mutually exclusive dichotomies
-   this is revealed by two questions that students commonly ask:

     (1) Is it physiological or is it psychological?   **(2) Is it inherited or is it learned?**

-   learning to ask the right questions is the first step to getting the right answers

2.   Current Thinking About the Biology of Behavior

   a. Is Behavior Physiological or Psychological? (see Fig. 2.1 – Fig. 2.2 in *BIOPSYCHOLOGY;* use *Digital Image Archive, Chpt 2. CH02F01.BMP)*

-   this idea grew out of a 16th century conflict between a growing scientific understanding of the world and the teachings of the Church; to resolve this tension, **Descartes** proposed that humans have 2 aspects: a **physical** one that can be studies scientifically, and a **mental** (mind) one that can only be understood by God. This came to be known as **Cartesian dualism.**
-   many people still believe that there is a purely psychological category of human existence (one that transcends physiology), but there is no evidence for this. Two lines of evidence bear on this question:
     1) brain manipulations can alter even the most complex psychological processes (e.g., Oliver Sacks' account of "the man who fell out of bed*)*; and
     2) nonhuman organisms possess abilities that many people once believed to be psychological and thus purely human (e.g., Gallup's studies of self-awareness in chimpanzees)
-   today, most scientists believe that physiological activity is the basis of psychological processes

b.   Is Behavior Inherited or Learned?

- the **nature-nurture** issue is an ancient one
- in this century, reflected in conflict between Watsonian **behaviorists** and European **ethologists**
- the discovery that factors other than genes and learning influence development (e.g., diet, stress, fetal environment) led to a reframing of the question; from "genes or learning?" to "genes or experience?"
- next it was argued that behavior always develops under the combined control of genes and experience, not one or the other; thus, the question became "How much is genetic, and how much is experience?" The problem is that genetics and experience are not additive, but rather interactive
- all behavioral development depends totally on genetics and totally on experience; modern biopsychologists study how they interact

c.   A 6-Stage Model of the Biology of Behavior (use **Digital Image Archive, Chpt 2. CH02F03**)

- using this figure, note the convoluted interaction between evolution, genes, and experience in the way an organism behaves in a given situation.

3.   Behavioral Development: The Interaction of Genetic Factors and Experience

- on behavioral development interactively. To help you, here are three examples:

a) Selective Breeding of "Maze-Bright" and "Maze-Dull" Rats

- Tryon raised **maze-bright** and **maze-dull** strains of rats; however, the maze-bright rats do better than the maze-dull rats only if they are both raised in **impoverished environments;** if they are both raised in enriched environments, the differences disappear
- maze-bright rats are not generally more intelligent, they do better because they are less emotional.

b) Phenylketonuria: A Single-Gene Metabolic Disorder

- a form of mental retardation that results from the accumulation of **phenylalanine** in the body
- due to absence of gene for **phenylalanine hydroxylase**, which converts phenylalanine to tyrosine
- sufferers develop disorder if they eat a phenylalanine-rich foods during development; diagnosed by high levels of **phenylpryruvic acid** in urine; treated by keeping sufferers on a phenylalanine-free diet during childhood.

c) Development of Bird Song (use *Digital Image Archive, Chpt 2., CH02F24.BMP)*

- some birds learn to sing by hearing conspecific songs early in life.
- research has revealed that birdsong develops in 2 stages: a **sensory phase** in which exposure to conspecific song leads to memories that later guide song development; and a **sensorimotor phase** in which birds must practice (and receive sensorimotor feedback) for songs to develop properly
- zebra finches and white-crowned sparrows are **age-limited learners**, meaning that once a bird develops an adult song it crystallizes, remaining unchanged for life. By contrast, male canaries are **open-ended learners**, meaning that they can add new songs to their repertoire each mating season.
- canary song circuit is remarkable in 4 ways: 1) it is **lateralized** to the left hemisphere (like human speech?); 2) the vocal center is 4X **larger in males** than in females; 3) in the spring, as new songs are acquired, the vocal centers **double in size**...only to shrink again in the fall; and 4) this growth is due to **neurogenesis...**a feat thought impossible in the adult vertebrate brain until very recently.

4. The Genetics of Human Psychological Differences: Twin Studies:

- to assess the relative contribution of genes and experience to the development of differences in psychological characteristics, researchers often study individuals with varying degrees of genetic similarity. For example, they might compare **identical (monozygotic) twins** (genetically identical) with **fraternal (dizygotic) twins** (no more the same than any sibs in a family).
- studies such as the **Minnesota Study** have found high correlations between the IQ's of identical twins separated at birth; **heritability estimates** based on these studies average about .70.

> Q: *What does this mean? Is IQ 70% genetic?*

A: *Heritability estimates estimate the proportion of variability in a particular trait that results from genetic variation...that is, the contribution of genetic differences to phenotypic differences between individuals. They do NOT estimate the relative contribution of genes versus environment to development.*

- there are no psychological differences that do not have a genetic component; it is important to keep in mind that genetics alter the development of behavior by influencing an organism's experience of its surroundings, causing individuals with similar genetic endowment to seek out similar environments and experiences.

Conclusions:

- behavior is not a consequence of physiology or psychology, or of nature or nurture...it is the product of neural activity shaped by interactions among genes, past experience, and an organism's present situation.

Suggested Websites for Lecture 2b

Development of Bird Song: *http://soma.npa.uiuc.edu/courses/neuroethol/models/birdsong_learning/bird_song.html*
A fabulous site describing the anatomy, physiology and development of bird song in the zebra finch...check out the audio sample of its song!

Twin Studies: *http://www.psych.umn.edu/psylabs/mtfs/*
A look at ongoing twins studies at the University of Minnesota.

Nature vs. Nurture: the Pendulum Still Swings With Plenty of Momentum *http://home.att.net/~xchar/tna/ledoux.htm*
From the Chronicle of Higher Education, an interesting article by Dr. Joseph E. LeDoux on the nature/nurture controversy.

---

*Thinking clearly about the biology of behavior is as important
in every-day life as it is in the biopsychology laboratory.*

IM-At-A-Glance. Chapter 3: The Anatomy of the Nervous System:
The Systems, Structures and Cells That Make Up Your Nervous System

Detailed Outline	Print Supplements	Media Supplements	Professor's Notes
Chapter 3 The Anatomy of the Nervous System: The Systems, Structures and Cells That Make Up Your Nervous System, pp. 51-78	**Instructor's Manual for** *BIOPSYCHOLOGY,* *Lecture 3a and* *Lecture 3b*	**Beyond the Brain &** **Behavior CD for** *BIOPSYCHOLOGY:* *The Nervous System* *module*	
3.1 General Layout of the Nervous System	**Test Bank for** *BIOPSYCHOLOGY,* *Chapter 3*	*Practice Tests for* *Chapter 3*	
3.2 Cells of the Nervous System		*Hard Copy for Chapter 3*	
3.3 Neuroanatomical Techniques & Directions	**Study Guide for** *BIOPSYCHOLOGY,* *Chapter 3*	*Electronic Flashcards for* *Chapter 3*	
3.4 The Spinal Cord	**Transparencies for Physiological Psychology:** *II. The Anatomy of the Nervous System*	**Digital Image Archive,** **Powerpoint Presentation** **and Bitmap Images for** *BIOPSYCHOLOGY:* *Chapter 3*	
3.5 The Five Major Divisions of the Brain			
3.6 Major Structures of the Brain		*BIOLOGICAL* *PSYCHOLOGY VIDEO:* *Segment 1.* The Human Brain	
		Segment 3. Anatomy of the Brain	

Lecture 3a

NEURONS, GLIA and
THE GENERAL LAYOUT of THE NERVOUS SYSTEM

Outline

1. **General Layout of the Nervous System: A System of Twos**
    a. CNS vs. PNS
    b. brain vs. spinal cord
    c. somatic vs. autonomic
    d. efferent vs. afferent
    e. sympathetic vs. parasympathetic

2. **The Meninges, Ventricles and the Blood-Brain Barrier**

3. **Cells of the Nervous System**
    a. Neurons
    b. Glial Cells and Satellite Cells

4. **Neuroanatomical Techniques**

Lecture Notes

1. **General Layout of the Nervous System** (see Fig. 3.1 – Fig. 3.2 in *BIOPSYCHOLOGY;* use *Digital Image Archive, Figures CH03F02.BMP* and *CH03F03.BMP*; use **The Nervous System** module from **Beyond the Brain & Behavior CD for** *BIOPSYCHOLOGY)*

    - the nervous system can be divided into **2 divisions** along several different criteria

        a. **CNS vs. PNS:** defined by the CNS being within the **bony skull** and **vertebral column**

        b. **brain vs. spinal cord:** comprise the 2 parts of the CNS

        c. **somatic vs. autonomic:** comprise the 2 parts of the PNS. The somatic branch interacts with the **external environment;** the autonomic branch interacts with the **internal environment.**

        d. **efferent vs. afferent:** refers to whether nerves bring **sensory information** into the CNS *(afferent)* or carry **motor commands** away from the CNS *(efferent)*

        e. **sympathetic vs. parasympathetic:** the two branches of the autonomic division of the PNS. Convention suggests that the sympathetic branch **activates** an organism while the parasympathetic branch acts to **conserve energy;** that each autonomic target organ is innervated by both branches; and that sympathetic activation indicates **arousal** while parasympathetic activation indicates **relaxation.**

    - the **cranial nerves** (see Appendix III) are a special group of nerves that leave the CNS from the brain, through the skull, rather than from the spinal cord. These have specific sensory and/or motor functions (see Appendix IV) disruption of these functions allow neurologists to accurately determine the location and size of tumors and other kinds of brain pathology.

2. **The Meninges, Ventricles and the Blood-Brain Barrier** *(*see Figure 3.3 and 3.4 in *BIOPSYCHOLOGY;* use *Digital Image Archive, Figures CH03F03.BMP* and *Figure CH03F04.BMP)*

- the brain and spinal cord are well-protected by the skull and vertebrae, and by three membranes called the **meninges**: the **dura mater** (*tough mother;* outside); the **arachnoid mater** (*spidery mother;* middle) and the **pia mater** (*gentle mother;* inside)

- **cerebrospinal fluid** (CSF) is manufactured by **choroid plexuses**, which are capillary networks that protrude into the ventricles; it circulates through the **ventricular system** of the brain, the **central canal** of the spinal cord, and the **subarachnoid space**; and it is absorbed into large channels called **sinuses** in the dura mater and then into the blood stream
- when the flow of CSF is blocked, **hydrocephalus** results
- most blood vessels of the brain do not readily allow compounds to pass from the general circulation into the brain; this protection, called the **blood-brain barrier,** is due to the tightly-packed nature of the cells of these blood vessels.

3. **Cells of the Nervous System** (see Figures 3.5, 3.6, 3.7, 3.8, 3.9, and 3.10 from *BIOPSYCHOLOGY;* use *Digital Image Archive, Figure CH03F05.BMP; Figure CH03F06.BMP; Figure CH03F07.BMP; Figure CH03F08.BMP;* and *Figure CH03F10.BMP)*

- the gross structures of the nervous system are made up of hundreds of billions of different cells that are either **neurons** or **glia.**

a. **Neurons**

- the fundamental functional unit of the nervous system; cells that are specialized for the reception, conduction and transmission of electrochemical signals.
- most of you have seen a schematic drawing of a multipolar motor neuron; don't be misled by its familiar shape, as neurons come in a wide variety of sizes and shapes. The following are its 9 parts:

1) a semipermeable **cell membrane.** The cell membrane is **semipermeable** because of special proteins that allows chemicals to cross the membrane; this semipermeability is critical to the normal activity of the neuron. The inside of the cell is filled with **cytoplasm.**

2) a **cell body** (soma) which is the metabolic center of the cell. The soma also contains the **nucleus** of the neuron, which contains cell's DNA.

3) **dendrites,** shorter processes emanating from the cell body that receive information from synaptic contacts with other neurons;

4) a single **axon,** that projects away from the cell body; this process may be as long as a meter!

5) **axon hillock,** the junction between cell body and axon; a critical structure in the conveyance of electrical signals by the neuron.

6) multiple **myelin sheaths.** These are formed by **oligodendroglia** in CNS and **Schwann** cells in PNS; they insulate the axon and assist in its conduction of electrical signals.

7) **nodes of Ranvier,** the small spaces between adjacent myelin sheaths;

8) **buttons,** the branched endings of the axon that release chemicals that allow the neuron to communicate with other cells; and

9) **synapses,** the points of communication between the neuron and other cells (neurons, muscle fibers).

- the type of neuron usually drawn in textbooks is called a **multipolar neuron,** because it has multiple dendrites and an axon extending from soma. There are also **unipolar neurons** (1 process combining both axon and dendrites off of the soma**), bipolar neurons** (a single axon and a single dendrite off the soma), and **interneurons** that have no axons at all.

    b.   **Glial Cells and Satellite Cells**

- the most common type of cells in the nervous system are **glia** and **satellite cells;** they outnumber neurons by as much as 10:1
- **glial cells** are found in the CNS and **satellite cells** in the PNS; they provide both physical and functional support to neurons
- the glial cells and satellite cells that form the myelin sheaths of axons in the CNS and PNS are **oligodendroglia** and **Schwann cells**, respectively.
- **astroglia** are the largest of the glial cells; they are found only in the CNS, where they support and provide nourishment for neurons.
- researchers have begun to appreciate that glia and satellite cells play a key role in the function of the nervous system; they help send chemical signals between neurons and they help to **establish and maintain connections** between neurons

4. Neuroanatomical Techniques (see Figures 3.11 – Figure 3.15 from *BIOPSYCHOLOGY)*

- research on the anatomy of the nervous system depends upon a variety of techniques that permit a clear view of different aspects of neural structure. These techniques include:

    i)   **Golgi Stain**: permitted **individual neurons** to be studied for the first time
    ii)   **Nissl Stain**: highlights **cell bodies of all neurons**; allowed estimation of cell density in tissue
    iii)   **Electron Microscopy**: allows visualization of the neuronal ultrastructure
    iv)   **Myelin Stain**: highlight **myelinated pathways;** less useful for studying individual axons
    v)   **Tract Tracing Techniques**: highlight **individual axons**; may be **retrograde** (trace back from terminal fields) or **anterograde** (trace from soma to terminal fields).

Suggested Websites for Lecture 3a:

Autonomic Nervous System: *http://www.ndrf.org/*
    The National Dysautonomia Research Foundation site; good overview of function and disorders like Shy-Drager Syndrome, Guillain Barre Syndrome, and more well-known disorders like diabetes and Parkinson's Disease.

Neurons and Glia: *http://faculty.washington.edu/chudler/introb.html*
    From Dr. Eric Chudler at the University of Washington; scroll down to "Neurons" to find information about neurons, glia, and a photo gallery of cells.

Neuroanatomy Quiz: *http://psych.hanover.edu/Krantz/neural/struct3.html*
    A quick quiz on the anatomy of the neuron; part of Dr John Krantz's study aids and tutorials for biopsychology.

The Ventricles: *http://www.epub.org.br/cm/n02/fundamentos/ventriculos_i.htm*
    From the Brain & Mind site, more information about ventricles, cerebrospinal fluid, and hydrocephalus.

Lecture 3b

THE GROSS ANATOMY
OF THE NERVOUS SYSTEM

Outline

1. **Orientation and Direction in the Vertebrate Nervous System**

2. **The Spinal Cord**

3. **The Five Major Divisions of the Brain**

   a. Myelencephalon
   b. Metencephalon
   c. Mesencephalon
   d. Diencephalon
   e. Telencephalon

Lecture Notes

1. **Orientation and Direction in the Vertebrate Nervous System** *(see Figure 3.16 and 3.17 in BIOPSYCHOLOGY; use Digital Image Archive, Chapter 3, Figure CH03F18.BMP)*

   - First axis: **anterior** means toward the nose or front; **posterior** means toward the tail or back
   - Second axis: **dorsal** is toward the surface of the back or top of the head (as in dorsal fin); **ventral** indicates the surface of the chest or bottom of the head
   - Third axis: **medial** is toward the midline of the body; **lateral** indicates outside or away from the midline

2. **The Spinal Cord** (see Fig. 3.19 and 3.20 in *BIOPSYCHOLOGY*; use *Digital Image Archive, Chapter 3, Figure CH03F19.BMP & Figure CH03F20.BMP*)

   - in cross section, the **gray matter** (cell bodies) forms a butterfly inside of the **white matter** (myelinated axons)
   - the upper (dorsal; posterior) wings of the butterfly are called the **dorsal horns;** the lower (ventral; anterior) wings are called the **ventral horns.**
   - 31 pairs of nerves are attached to the spinal cord; as they near the cord, they split into **dorsal roots** (sensory axons; cell bodies lie just outside the spinal cord in the **dorsal root ganglia**) or **ventral roots** (motor axons; cell bodies lie in the ventral horns)

3. **The Five Major Divisions of the Brain** (a brain model is useful for teaching this section; see Fig. 3.21 and 3.22 in *BIOPSYCHOLOGY*; use *Digital Image Archive, Figure CH03F21.BMP* and *Figure CH03F22.BMP*)

   - there are **five divisions** of the mammalian brain; in general, higher structures are less reflexive and more complex functions, and they are more recently evolved
   - the nervous system is first recognizable in the developing embryo as the **neural tube**
   - the brain develops from three swellings at one end of the neural tube: the **hind brain,** the **midbrain**, and the **forebrain**
   - the hind brain develops into the **myelencephalon** and the **metencephalon**; the forebrain develops into the **diencephalon** and the **telencephalon** (also called the **cerebral hemispheres**)
   - the term **"brain stem"** refers to the stem on which the cerebral hemispheres rest (myelencephalon + metencephalon + mesencephalon + diencephalon = brain stem)

The Five Main Divisions of the Nervous System:

a. **Myelencephalon** (see Fig. 3.23 in *BIOPSYCHOLOGY*; use *Digital Image Archive, Figure CH03F23.BMP)*

-   the myelencephalon is commonly called the **medulla**; it is composed of major ascending and descending tracts and a network of small nuclei involved in sleep, attention, muscle tone, cardiac function, and respiration
-   the core network of nuclei is the **reticular formation**; the reticular formation also composes the core of the hindbrain and midbrain; it is thought to be an arousal system and is sometimes called the **reticular activating system** (reticulum means "little net")

b. **Metencephalon** (see Fig. 3.23 in *BIOPSYCHOLOGY*; use *Digital Image Archive, Figure CH03F23.BMP)*

-   the metencephalon has two parts: the **cerebellum** (little brain) and **pons** (bridge)
-   the cerebellum has both **sensorimotor** and **cognitive functions;** the pons is visible as a swelling on the inferior surface; it also contains the **reticular formation**
-   neural tracts ascend and descend through this area

c. **Mesencephalon** (see Fig. 3.24 in *BIOPSYCHOLOGY*; use *Digital Image Archive, Figure CH03F24.BMP)*

-   the mesencephalon is composed of the **tectum** and **tegmentum**
-   in mammals, the tectum consists of the **superior colliculi** (visual relay) and the **inferior colliculi** (auditory relay); in lower vertebrates there is simply a single **optic tectum**
-   the tegmentum contains the reticular formation, the **red nucleus** (sensorimotor), the **substantia nigra** (sensorimotor; cell bodies here die in patients with Parkinson's Disease); and the **periaqueductal gray** (mediates analgesia)

d. **Diencephalon** (see Fig. 3.25 and 3.26 and Appendix V in *BIOPSYCHOLOGY*; use *Digital Image Archive, Figure CH03F25.BMP)*

-   the **thalamus** and **hypothalamus** are the two main structures of the diencephalon
-   the thalamus is the top of the brain stem; it is comprised of many different nuclei, most of which project to cortex
-   some thalamic nuclei are **sensory relay nuclei**; (e.g., **lateral geniculate nuclei**, vision; **medial geniculate nuclei**, audition; **ventral posterior nuclei**, touch)
-   the **hypothalamus** is just below the thalamus ("hypo" means below); the **pituitary gland** (snot gland) is suspended from the hypothalamus; together, the hypothalamus and pituitary play key roles in endocrine function and many motivated behaviors
-   the **mammillary bodies** are two small bumps visible on the inferior surface, just behind the hypothalamus
-   the **optic chiasm** is the X-shaped part of the optic nerves that lies just in front of the pituitary; it is the spot where axons that originate from the nasal half of each retina cross over (**decussate**) to the opposite side of the brain

e. **Telencephalon** *(*see Fig.3.27, 3.28, and 3.29 in *BIOPSYCHOLOGY*; use *Digital Image Archive, Figure CH03F27.BMP, CH03F28.BMP* and *CH03F29.BMP)*

-   also called the cerebral hemispheres; characterized by the cortex (bark) with its many convolutions, which are referred to as **gyri** (like hills) or **fissures** (like valleys).
-   the telencephalon is the largest division of human brain; large tracts called **commissures** connect the two hemispheres; the **corpus callosum** is the largest commissure
-   the telencephalon mediates most **complex cognitive functions**
-   about 90% of human cortex is **neocortex,** comprised of **6 cell layers** of **pyramidal cells** and **stellate cells**

- the hippocampus is not neocortex; instead, it is a 3-layer cortical area that lies in the medial temporal lobe
- the **four lobes** of the cerebral hemispheres are defined by the fissures of the cerebral cortex. The four lobes are:

    i) **frontal lobe:** superior to the **lateral fissure** and anterior to the **central fissure;**
    ii) **temporal lobe:** inferior to the lateral fissure
    iii) **parietal lobe:** posterior to the central fissure
    iv) **occipital lobe:** posterior to the temporal lobe and the parietal lobe

- note the following useful neocortical landmarks: **longitudinal fissure** (between the hemispheres), precentral gyri (in frontal lobe; primary motor cortex), **postcentral gyri** (in parietal lobe; primary somatosensory cortex), **superior temporal gyri** (in the temporal lobe; auditory cortex), and **prefrontal cortex** (the nonmotor portion of the frontal lobe)

- most of the subcortical parts of the telencephalon are axonal pathways; however, two subcortical systems exist that play important roles in determining our behavior. These are:

    i)   *Limbic System* (see Fig. 3.30 in ***BIOPSYCHOLOGY;*** use *Digital Image Archive, Figure CH03F30.BMP):*

    - involved in **regulation of motivated behaviors** (including the "Four F's"!); includes the **mammillary bodies, hippocampus; amygdala; fornix; cingulate cortex** and **septum.**

    i)   *The Basal Ganglia* (see Fig. 3.31 in ***BIOPSYCHOLOGY;*** use *Digital Image Archive, Figure CH03F31.BMP):*

    - involved in **movement;** include the **amygdala** (again!); the **caudate** and **putamen** (collectively called the **striatum**); and the **globus pallidum.**

YOUR ABILITY TO UNDERSTAND BRAIN/BEHAVIOR RELATIONS WILL BE GREATLY FACILITATED IF YOU HAVE A GOOD UNDERSTANDING OF THE BASIC ANATOMY PRESENTED HERE...REVIEW IT!!!

Suggested Websites for Lecture 3b:

Interactive Brain Atlas: *http://www9.biostr.washington.edu/da.html*
From the Digital Anatomist project at the University of Washington, select the "BRAIN" icon for a fabulous collection of images in many different planes of section, digital recreations of different functional systems in the brain, and a good section on cerebrovasculature.

Word Roots: *http://faculty.washington.edu/chudler/neuroroot.html*
A good source for the Greek and Latin roots of many neuroanatomical terms.

IM-At-A-Glance. Chapter 4: Neural Conduction and Synaptic Transmission:
How Neurons Send and Receive Signals

Detailed Outline	Print Supplements	Media Supplements	Professor's Notes
Chapter 4. Neural Conduction and Synaptic Transmission: How Neurons Send and Receive Signals, pp. 79-103	**Instructor's Manual for** *BIOPSYCHOLOGY, Lecture 4a and Lecture 4b*	**Beyond the Brain & Behavior CD for** *BIOPSYCHOLOGY: Ion Channels module* *Ionic Basis of the Resting Membrane Potential module*	
4.3 The Neuron's Resting Membrane Potential	**Test Bank for** *BIOPSYCHOLOGY, Chapter 4*	*Interactions Between EPSPs and IPSPs module;*	
4.4 Generation & Conduction of Postsynaptic Potentials		*Summation of EPSPs module*	
4.3 Integration of Postsynaptic Potentials and Generation of Action Potentials	**Study Guide for** *BIOPSYCHOLOGY, Chapter 4*	*Integration of PSPs module* *Generation of the Action Potential module*	
4.4 Conduction of Action Potentials	**Transparencies for Physiological Psychology:** *III. Electrical and Chemical Signals in the Nervous System*	*Ionic Basis of the Action Potential module* *Synaptic Transmission Animation*	
4.5 Synaptic Transmission: Chemical Transmission of Signals from One Neuron to Another		*Review of Synaptic Transmission module* *Amino Acid Synapses Module*	
4.6 The Neurotransmitters		*Action at the Synapse module*	
4.7 Pharmacology of Synaptic Transmission		*Practice Tests for Chapter 4* *Hard Copy for Chapter 4* *Electronic Flashcards for Chapter 4* **Digital Image Archive, Powerpoint Presentation and Bitmap Images for** *BIOPSYCHOLOGY: Chapter 4*	

Lecture 4a

NEURAL CONDUCTION

Outline:

1. **Measuring the Membrane Potential**

2. **The Ionic Basis of the Resting Membrane Potential**

3. **Four Factors Determine the Ionic Distribution that Underlies the Resting Membrane Potential**
   a. Random Motion
   b. Electrostatic Pressure
   c. Differential Permeability of the Membrane
   d. Sodium-Potassium Pumps

4. **Postsynaptic Potentials**

5. **Generation of Action Potentials**

6. **Ionic Events Underlying Action Potentials**

7. **Conduction of Action Potentials**
   a. Action Potentials are Nondecremental and Slow
   b. Myelin Increases the Speed of Conduction

8. **Changing Views on Dendritic Function**

Lecture Notes

1. **Measuring the Membrane Potential** (use *Digital Image Archive, CH04F02.BMP)*

   - to learn how information is sent from the dendrites and soma of a neuron to its terminals, researchers study a neuron's **membrane potential** (the difference in electrical charge between the inside and the outside of the neuron).
   - to record a membrane potential two electrodes are needed: an **intracellular** electrode and an **extracellular** electrode
   - intracellular electrodes must be **microelectrodes**; they are usually made from **saline-filled micropipettes** by heating and pulling apart a fine glass tube with an **electrode puller**

2. **The Ionic Basis of the Resting Membrane Potential** (see Figure 4.1 2 in *BIOPSYCHOLOGY;* use *Digital Image Archive, CH04F03.BM;* use **Ion Channels** module from the *BEYOND THE BRAIN & BEHAVIOR CD)*

   - when both intracellular and extracellular electrodes are outside a neuron, the difference between the electrical potentials at their tips is zero; when the intracellular electrode penetrates the neuron, the potential jumps to about **-70 millivolts** (the inside is 70 millivolts less than the outside)
   - this is the **resting potential** of the neuron
   - the resting potential exists because positively and negatively charged ions are distributed unequally on the two sides of the neural membrane: the concentration of Na^+ and Cl- are higher outside the neuron, and the concentration of K^+ and various negatively charged **proteins** are higher inside the neuron

3. Four Factors Determine the Ionic Distribution That Underlies the Resting Potential (see Fig. 4.2 in *BIOPSYCHOLOGY;* use *Digital Image Archive, CH04F04.BMP*; use **Ionic Basis of the Resting Membrane Potential** module from the *BEYOND THE BRAIN & BEHAVIOR CD*)

- four factors interact to produce the resting membrane potential; two **passive** (non-energy-consuming) factors act to distribute ions equally across the membrane (**homogenizing factors**), and one passive and one active factor act to distribute ions unequally across the membrane

a. **Random Motion** (passive)
   - ions in solution are in random motion
   - thus, any time that there is an accumulation of a particular class of ions in one area, the probability is increased that random motion will move ions out of this area (because there are more ions available to leave) and the probability is decreased that random motion will move more ions into the area (because there are fewer ions available to come in)

b. **Electrostatic Pressure** (passive)
   - **like charges repel** and **opposite charges attract;** therefore electrostatic pressure disperses any accumulation of positive or negative charges in an area

c. **Differential Permeability of the Membrane** (passive)
   - ions pass through membrane at special pores called **ion channels**
   - when neurons are at rest, the membrane is: totally resistant to the passage of protein ions, extremely resistant to the passage of Na^+ ions, and only slightly resistant to the passage of K+ ions and Cl⁻ ions

d. **Sodium-Potassium Pumps** (active)
   - active (energy-consuming) mechanisms in the neural membrane continuously transfer Na^+ ions out of the neuron and K^+ ions in
   - this occurs at a ratio of 3 Na+ ions moved out for every 2 K+ ions moved in; thus, there is a loss of 1 positive charge every time the pump is activated

4. Postsynaptic Potentials (see Fig. 4.3 from *BIOPSYCHOLOGY;* use **Interactions Between EPSPs and IPSPs** module from the *BEYOND THE BRAIN & BEHAVIOR CD*)

- now that you understand the state of resting neurons, let's see how electrical signals are created in them
- **postsynaptic potentials** are changes in the membrane potential produced by the action of **neurotransmitters** released by **presynaptic neurons**
- **excitatory postsynaptic potentials** (EPSPs) are **depolarizations**; they increase the likelihood that a neuron will fire
- **inhibitory postsynaptic potentials** (IPSPs) are **hyperpolarizations;** they decrease the likelihood that a neuron will fire
- postsynaptic potentials have three important properties:

   i) they are **graded** (their amplitude is proportional to the intensity of the input; that is, stronger stimuli produce bigger EPSPs and IPSPs);
   ii) they are transmitted **decrementally** (as they passively spread from their site of generation, they get weaker as they go, like sound through air); and
   iii) they are **transmitted rapidly** (like electricity through a cable, so rapidly that transmission is usually regarded as being instantaneous)

5. **Generation of Action Potentials** (see Fig. 4.4 and 4.5 from *BIOPSYCHOLOGY;* use *Digital Image Archive,* *CH04F06.BMP* and *CH04F07.BMP;* use **Summation of EPSPs** and **Integration of PSPs** modules from the *BEYOND THE BRAIN & BEHAVIOR CD)*

- **action potentials** (APs; neuron firing) are triggered at the **axon hillock** when a neuron is depolarized to the point that the membrane potential at the axon hillock reaches about **-65 mV**; this is the **threshold of excitation** for many neurons
- unlike EPSPs and IPSPs, APs are **not graded**; they are **all-or-none** (they occur full blown or not at all)
- most neurons receive hundreds of synaptic contacts; what happens at any one synapse has very little effect on the firing of the neuron; whether or not a neuron fires is determined by the adding together (integration) of what goes on at many neurons
- there are **two kinds of neural integration:**

    i) **spatial summation:** which can involve EPSPs + EPSPs; IPSPs + IPSPs; or EPSPs + IPSPs; and

    ii) **temporal summation:** which can involve EPSPs + EPSPs or IPSPs + IPSPs.

    NOTE THAT EPSPs AND IPSPs CANNOT TEMPORALLY SUMMATE...due to the fact that just a single synapse is involved, and it must be either excitatory or inhibitory but not both.

- in a functioning neuron, both spatial and temporal summation go on continuously; synapses closer to the **axon hillock** have a larger effect on firing due to the decremental transmission of postsynaptic potentials

6. **Ionic Events Underlying Action Potentials** (see Fig. 4.6 from *BIOPSYCHOLOGY;* use *Digital Image Archive, CH04F08.BMP;* see the **Generation of the Action Potential** module from the *BEYOND THE BRAIN & BEHAVIOR CD)*

- when the threshold of excitation (about -65mV) is reached, **voltage-gated Na^+ channels** open momentarily, and Na^+ ions rush into the neuron under tremendous pressure from both their concentration gradient and the electrostatic gradient; this drives the membrane potential to about +50 millivolts
- at the same time, **voltage-gated K^+ channels** slowly begin to open. Most of these channels open at about the time that the membrane potential is about +50 mV. At this point, K^+ ions are driven out by the +50 millivolt charge and by their high internal concentration; this repolarizes the neuron and leaves it slightly **hyperpolarized** for a few milliseconds.
- because only a few ions adjacent to the membrane are involved in the generation of an action potential, the resting potential is readily reestablished by the random motion of ions (AND NOT THE NA+/K+ PUMP!)
- for 1-2 milliseconds after an action potential is generated, another action potential cannot be generated no matter what kind of input that neuron receives; this is called the **absolute refractory period.** This is followed by the **relative refractory period,** during which time an action potential can only be elicited by high levels of stimulation

7. **Conduction of Action Potentials** (see Fig. 4.6 from *BIOPSYCHOLOGY;* use *Digital Image Archive, CH04F08.BMP;* see the **Generation of the Action Potential** module from the *BEYOND THE BRAIN & BEHAVIOR CD)*

    a. Action Potentials are Nondecremental and Slow

    - once an AP is generated at the axon hillock, it is transmitted along the axon; the purpose of axons is to transmit APs from the soma to the terminal buttons of the neuron
    - conduction of APs along an axon is not like the transmission of PSPs; conduction of EPSPs and IPSPs is **passive** (like electricity through a cable), thus it is **instantaneous** and **decremental;** whereas conduction of an AP along an axon is **active**, and therefore **slower** and **nondecremental**
    - when voltage-gated Na+ channels on the hillock membrane open, Na^+ ions rush in and a full blown AP is generated

- the electrical disturbance that is created is transmitted passively to the next Na+ channels along the axon; in response, the voltage-gated Na+ channels there open and another full-blown potential is generated
- in reality, the sodium channels are so tightly packed that it is best to think of APs as waves of depolarization spreading down an axon; the AP is regenerated along the length of the axon
- APs also spread from the hillock back through the cell body and dendrites, but because the ion channels in the cell body and dendrites are **chemical-gated** rather than voltage-gated, transmission of action potentials through cell bodies and dendrites is passive
- transmission in the normal direction, from the hillock to the terminal buttons, is called **orthodromic conduction;** however, if the terminals are electrically stimulated, APs can be generated and actively transmitted back to the hillock; this is called **antidromic conduction**

b. Myelin Increases the Speed of Conduction

- many axons are myelinated by **oligodendroglia** in the CNS and by **Schwann cells** in the PNS; myelination insulates the semipermeable axon membrane blocking the flow of ions through the axon at all but the **nodes of Ranvier**; paradoxically this actually improves transmission
- in myelinated axons, APs travel passively (decrementally and rapidly) between the nodes of Ranvier; but at each node there is a "pause" while a full-blown AP is generated
- this is called **saltatory conduction** ("saltatory" means to skip or jump); because much of the transmission of APs in myelinated axons is passive (from node to node), transmission in myelinated axons is faster and it requires less energy
- larger axons conduct faster; myelinated axons conduct faster

Changing Views on Dendritic Function

- dendritic function is more complex than was previously believed; for example, dendrites appear to be able to actively conduct action potentials, and many dendritic signals appear to be compartmentalized (restricted) to just certain parts of the dendritic tree
- the functional significance of these abilities remains to be determined; however, dendrites are clearly more than just passive conductors of action potentials

Suggest Websites for Lecture 4a:

The Action Potential: *http://faculty.washington.edu/chudler/ap.html*
> From Dr. Chudler's excellent site at the University of Washington, a description of the action potential complete with the an animation and the "sounds" of an action potential.

Action Potential Animations: *http://psych.hanover.edu/Krantz/neural/actionpotential.html*
> From Dr. John Krantz at Hanover College, an animation of the physical factors involved in the action potential. A good introduction to ions, diffusion, complete with quizzes.

Virtual Electrophysiology Lab: *http://www.hhmi.org/grants/lectures/biointeractive/vlabs/index.htm*
> From the Howard Hughes Medical Institute; select the Neurophysiology Lab for some a virtual lab using the leech.

Lecture 4b

SYNAPTIC TRANSMISSION

Outline:

1. **Synaptic Contacts and Transmission**
   a. Structure of Synapses
   b. Synthesis, Packing & Transport of Neurotransmitter Molecules
   c. Release of Neurotransmitter Molecules
   d. Activation of Receptors
   e. Reuptake, Degradation and Recycling

2. **Neurotransmitters and Receptors**
   a. Amino Acid Neurotransmitters
   b. Monoamine Neurotransmitters
   c. Acetylcholine
   d. Soluble Gas Neurotransmitters
   e. Neuropeptide Neurotransmitters

3. **Pharmacology of Synaptic Transmission**

Lecture Notes

1. **Synaptic Contacts and Transmission** (see Fig. 4.7 in *BIOPSYCHOLOGY;* use *Digital Image Archive, CH04F09.BMP*; use **Synaptic Transmission** module from the *BEYOND THE BRAIN & BEHAVIOR CD;* use **Neurons & Synaptic Transmission** from the *BIOLOGICAL PSYCHOLOGY* video*)*

   a. **Structure of Synapses**

   - in addition to axosomatic and axodendritic synapses there are: (1) **axoaxonic** synapses, (2) **dendrodendritic** synapses, (3) **dendroaxonic** synapses, (4) synapses between the main shafts of axons, (5) **nondirected synapses**
   - some dendrodendritic synapses are **reciprocal** (they can transmit in either direction)
   - many neurons have **autoreceptors** in their presynaptic membranes; these are stimulated by the neuron's own neurotransmitter and are thought to mediate negative feedback
   - some synapses occur on little buds on dendrites; these buds are called **dendritic spines**; other dendritic synapses occur right on the dendrite shaft
   - axoaxonic synapses mediate **presynaptic inhibition; postsynaptic inhibition** is mediated by axodendritic and axosomatic synapses
   - most synapses that are discussed in textbooks are **directed synapses** (synapses where the site of release and the target site are in close apposition)
   - there are also **nondirected synapses**; for example, some presynaptic axons have a **string-of-beads** appearance and the neurotransmitter is widely dispersed from each bead to many targets in the general area; this arrangement is common for monoamines

   b. **Synthesis, Packing & Transport of Neurotransmitter Molecules** (see Fig. 4.7 in *BIOPSYCHOLOGY;* use *Digital Image Archive, CH04F09.BMP*; use **Synaptic Transmission** and **Action at the Synapse** modules from the *BEYOND THE BRAIN & BEHAVIOR CD)*

   - there are 2 main types of neurotransmitters: **small-molecule transmitters,** synthesized in the cytoplasm and packed into **vesicles** by the **Golgi complex;** and **large-molecule transmitters,** synthesized in the soma by **ribosomes** and then moved down to the terminals by **microtubules**
   - there can be small- and large-molecule transmitters in the same terminal button; this is called **coexistence**

c. **Release of Neurotransmitter Molecules** (see Fig. 4.10 in *BIOPSYCHOLOGY;* use **Synaptic Transmission** and **Action at the Synapse** modules from the *BEYOND THE BRAIN & BEHAVIOR CD)*

- the arrival of an AP at a terminal button opens **voltage-gated calcium channels** in the button membrane, and Ca^{++} ions enter the button
- the entry of the Ca^{++} ions causes the synaptic vesicles to fuse with the **presynaptic membrane** and empty their contents into the **synaptic cleft**--a process called **exocytosis**
- small-molecule transmitters are usually released each time an action potential arrives at the terminal; by contrast, large-molecule transmitters are released gradually in response to multiple action potentials

d. **Activation of Receptors** (see Fig. 4.11 in *BIOPSYCHOLOGY;* use *Digital Image Archive, CH04F13.BMP*; use **Synaptic Transmission** and **Action at the Synapse** modules from the *BEYOND THE BRAIN & BEHAVIOR CD)*

- after its release, neurotransmitters diffuses across the synaptic cleft to the **post-synaptic membrane**; there it binds to **receptors** for it in the postsynaptic membrane; there are **specific receptors** for each neurotransmitter

- the binding of the neurotransmitter to its receptors can influence the postsynaptic neuron in one of two fundamentally different ways:

    i)   it can act at an **ionotropic receptor** directly associated with a channel in the postsynaptic membrane and induce brief EPSPs or IPSPs; or
    ii)   it can act at an **metabotropic receptor** associated with a signal protein that is attached to a **G-protein** inside the neuron; this G-protein can either move to a nearby ion channel, activate it, and cause a change in the membrane potential OR it can lead to the production of chemicals, called **secondary messengers** which can have more enduring and far-reaching effects on the sensitivity of the neuron

e. **Reuptake, Degradation and Recycling** (see Fig. 4.12 in *BIOPSYCHOLOGY;* use *Digital Image Archive, CH04F14.BMP*; use **Review of Synaptic Transmission** from the *BEYOND THE BRAIN & BEHAVIOR CD*

- neurotransmitters are **deactivated** in the synapse by one of two mechanisms:

    i)   some transmitters are broken down in the synapse by enzymes;,;
    ii)   other neurotransmitters are deactivated by **reuptake** into the presynaptic neuron, where they are recycled

2. **Neurotransmitters and Receptors** (see Fig. 4.13 – 4.15 in *BIOPSYCHOLOGY;* use *Digital Image Archive, CH04F17.BMP*; use **The Amino Acid Synapses** module from the *BEYOND THE BRAIN & BEHAVIOR CD)*

a.   **Amino Acid Neurotransmitters**

   - amino acids are the individual building blocks of proteins; they also serve as the transmitters at fast-acting, point-to-point synapses
   - there is conclusive evidence that **glutamate, aspartate, glycine**, and gamma-aminobutyric acid **(GABA)** are neurotransmitters
   - glutamate, aspartate, and glycine come from the proteins that we eat; GABA is synthesized from glutamate

   b.   **Monoamine Neurotransmitters**

- monoamine neurotransmitters are formed by slight modification to amino acid molecules; thus the name "monoamine" (one amine)
- they are often released from **string-of-beads** axons, and they have slow, lingering, diffuse effects; neurons that release monoamines typically have their cell bodies in the brain stem
- there are **four monoamine neuro**transmitters and they belong to one of **two subclasses:**

   1) **catecholamine** neurotransmitters: these include **dopamine, norepinephrine,** and **epinephrine**; all three are synthesized from the amino acid **tyrosine**; tyrosine is converted to L-DOPA, to dopamine, to norepinephrine, to epinephrine
   2) **indolamine** neurotransmitter: **serotonin**; synthesized from the amino acid **tryptophan**

   b.   *Acetylcholine*

- **acetylcholine (ACh)** is the small molecule transmitter at neuromuscular junctions, at many synapses in the ANS, and at some CNS synapses; it is created by addition of an **acetyl group** to a **choline** molecule; thus the name
- acetylcholine is the only neurotransmitter known to be deactivated in the synapse by enzymatic degradation rather than by reuptake; it is deactivated by **acetylcholinesterase**

   d.   *Soluble Gas Neurotransmitters*

- this class of recently identified neurotransmitters includes **nitric oxide** and **carbon monoxide**
- the gasses are produced in the neural cytoplasm, diffuse immediately through the cell membrane into the extracellular fluid and into nearby cells to stimulate production of second messengers
- they are difficult to study as they act rapidly and are immediately broken down, existing for only a few seconds

   e.   *Neuropeptide Transmitters*

- peptides are short chains of 10 or fewer amino acids; over 50 peptides are **putative neurotransmitters**; they are the largest neurotransmitters
- **endorphins** are an example of a neuropeptide transmitter; they are opiate-like transmitters that are important to analgesia and reward systems in the brain

3. Pharmacology of Synaptic Transmission (see Fig. 4.16 – 4.18 in *BIOPSYCHOLOGY;* use *Digital Image Archive, CH04F18.BMP, CH04F19.BMP, and CH04F20.BMP)*

- drugs that facilitate a transmitter's effects are called **agonists;** drugs that reduce a transmitter's effects are called **antagonists**
- drugs act upon one or more of the **7 steps in neurotransmitter action;** the exact mechanism varies from drug to drug
- for example, **cocaine** is a **catecholamine agonist** that acts by blocking the reuptake of **dopamine** and **norepinephrine**
- by contrast, **valium** is a GABA agonist that acts by increasing the binding of GABA to its receptor
- **atropine** and **curare** are both Ach antagonists; atropine blocks **muscarinic receptors**, whereas curare paralyzes by blocking **nicotinic receptors**

Suggested Websites for Lecture 4b:

Neurotransmitters & Neuroactive Peptides: *http://faculty.washington.edu/chudler/chnt1.html*
   From Dr. Eric Chudler at the University of Washington, a good overview of these neurotransmitter subtypes.

IM-At-A-Glance. Chapter 5: The Research Methods of Biopsychology: Understanding What Biopsychologists Do

Detailed Outline	Print Supplements	Media Supplements	Professor's Notes
Chapter 5. **The Research Methods of Biopsychology:** Understanding What Biopsychologists Do, pp. 104-131	**Instructor's Manual for** *BIOPSYCHOLOGY,* *Lecture 5a and* *Lecture 5b*	**Beyond the Brain & Behavior CD for** *BIOPSYCHOLOGY:* *Practice Tests for Chapter 5*	
Part One: Methods of Studying the Nervous System	**Test Bank for** *BIOPSYCHOLOGY,* *Chapter 5*	*Hard Copy for Chapter 5* *Electronic Flashcards for Chapter 5*	
5.1 Methods of Visualizing the Living Human Brain	**Study Guide for** *BIOPSYCHOLOGY,* *Chapter 5*	**Digital Image Archive, Powerpoint Presentation and Bitmap Images for** *BIOPSYCHOLOGY:* *Chapter 5*	
5.2 Recording Human Psychophysical Activity			
5.3 Invasive Physiological Research Methods	**Transparencies for Physiological Psychology:** *IV. Methods for Studying Brain & Behavior*		
5.4 Pharmacological Research Methods		*BIOLOGICAL PSYCHOLOGY VIDEO:* *Segment 5. The Electroencephalogram*	
5.5 Genetic Engineering			
Part Two. Behavioral Research Methods of Biopsychology			
5.6 Neuropsychological Testing			
5.7 Behavioral Methods of Cognitive Neuroscience			
5.8 Biopsychological Paradigms of Animal Behavior			

Lecture 5a

METHODS OF STUDYING THE NERVOUS SYSTEM

Outline

1. Methods of Visualizing the Living Human Brain
   a. Contrast X-rays
   b. Computerized Axial Tomography
   c. Magnetic Resonance Imaging
   d. Positron Emission Tomography
   e. Functional MRI
   f. Magnetoencephalography

2. Recording Psychophysiological Signals
   a. Scalp Electroencephalography
   b. Measures of Somatic Nervous System Activity
   c. Autonomic Nervous System Activity

3. Invasive Physiological and Pharmacological Methods
   a. Stereotaxic Surgery
   b. Lesion Methods
   c. Electrical Stimulation
   d. Electrical Recording Methods
   e. Pharmacological Methods

4. Genetic Engineering
   a. Knockouts
   b. Gene replacement

Lecture Notes

1. **Methods of Visualizing the Living Human Brain**

   - methods in this section explain how the nervous systems of living humans and animals can be studied

   a. Contrast X-rays: (see Fig. 5.1 in *BIOPSYCHOLOGY*)

   - to take an X-ray photograph of an object, a beam of X-rays is passed through it onto a photographic plate; any part of the object that absorbs X-rays differently than does the surrounding medium will be distinguishable
   - standard X-rays can't be used for studying the brain because the brain is composed of many overlapping structures that all absorb X-rays to about the same degree
   - **contrast X-ray** solve this problem in some cases; a **radio-opaque material** is introduced into the structure of interest to make it "stand out" from the others on an X-ray photograph
   - for example, in **cerebral angiography** a radio-opaque dye is injected into the **carotid artery;** it reveals displacement or enlargement of blood vessels

b. **Computerized Tomography** (CT) (see Fig. 5.2 in *BIOPSYCHOLOGY*)

- provides a **3-dimensional** view of a structure
- the X-ray gun and the X-ray detector rotate in apposition around the brain at one level taking a series of measurements from which an image of one section is constructed; this is repeated at **multiple levels**
- the CT-scan image of the brain is not **high-resolution**

c. **Magnetic Resonance Imaging** (MRI) (see Fig. 5.3, Fig. 5.4 and Fig. 5.5 in *BIOPSYCHOLOGY*)

- it has **higher resolution than CT**
- the images are created from measurements of the waves emitted by **hydrogen atoms** when they are placed in a magnetic field; its clarity stems from the fact that neural structures differ considerably in their density of hydrogen atoms

d. **Positron Emission Tomography (PET)** (see Fig. 5.6 in *BIOPSYCHOLOGY*)

- a method of highlighting brain areas that are **active,** rather than equally showing all brain structures
- the patient is injected with **radio-active 2-deoxyglucose**; because 2-DG is structurally similar to glucose, it is taken up by neurons as if it were glucose
- more active neurons need more energy and take up more 2-DG; unlike glucose, 2-DG cannot be metabolized by neurons and it **accumulates** in them
- the patient is injected with radio-active 2-DG and then engages in the activity under study (e.g., reading) while a **PET scan** of the brain is being taken
- the PET scan reveals on a series of images of horizontal sections where radio-activity has accumulated, and thus it indicates what areas were particularly active during the test

e. **Functional MRI** (see Fig. 5.7 in *BIOPSYCHOLOGY*)

- allows brain activity to be measured by imaging the increase in oxygen (blood) flow that occurs to brain areas that are active
- its four advantages over PET include (1) **nothing must be injected** into the subject, (2) one image provides **structural and functional** formation, (3) the **spatial resolution is better**, and (4) changes can be measured in **real time**

f. **Magnetoencephalography (MEG)**

- measures brain activity in terms of changes in magnetic fields measured on the surface of the scalp

2. **Recording Psychophysiological Signals**

a. **Scalp Electroencephalography (EEG):** (see Fig. 5.8 - Fig. 5.11 in *BIOPSYCHOLOGY; use Digital Image Archive Figure CH05F07.BMP, CH05F09.BMP; CH05F10.BMP ; use Segment 5. The Electroencephalogram of the BIOLOGICAL PSYCHOLOGY video)*

- an EEG signal is measured through an array of **scalp electrodes**
- EEG waves reflect the **sum total** of all of the electrical events in the head (APs, EPSPs, IPSPs, eye movements, blood flow, etc.); thus the EEG reveals little about the nature of the underlying neural activity
- its value lies in the fact that particular EEG wave forms are associated with particular states of **consciousness;** generally **low-amplitude, fast EEG** activity is associated with an **alert** aroused state; and **high-amplitude, slow EEG** activity (alpha waves) is associated with a **relaxed** but awake state
- EEG can be used to study brain activity in real time, in response to specific events. These are called **evoked potentials**. Usually, many evoked potentials are used to generate an **averaged evoked potential** in order to reduce the noise of the background EEG activity.
- EEG recordings are a valuable diagnostic tool; for example, the presence of high-amplitude spikes in the EEG (i.e., **epileptic spikes**) is the primary criterion for diagnosing epilepsy

b. **Measures of Somatic Nervous System Activity**

    i) **Muscle Tension** (see Fig. 5.12 in *BIOPSYCHOLOGY;* use *Digital Image Archive Figure CH05F11.BMP)*

- an **electromyogram (EMG)** is the changing difference in the voltage between two large electrodes placed on the skin above a large muscle; the amplitude of EMG signals indicates the combined level of tension in the underlying muscle
- the raw signals are usually **integrated** so that the data are easier to work with; the height of the curve of integrated EMG activity indicates the number of spikes in the EMG signal per unit of time

    ii) **Eye Movement** (see Fig. 5.13 in *BIOPSYCHOLOGY)*

- in an **electrooculogram (EOG),** eye movements are recorded by placing four electrodes around the eye; the signal results from the fact that the front of eye is more positively charged than the back
- the direction of movement can be inferred from the relation between the activity recorded on two channels: (1) above vs. below and (2) left vs. right

c. **Autonomic Nervous System Activity**

    i) **Skin Conductance:**

- **skin conductance level** (SCL) is the general level of skin conductance associated with a particular situation
- a **skin conductance response** (SCR) is a rapid change in skin conductance in response to a particular event; one application is the lie detector test

    i) **Cardiovascular Activity**

- **heart rate;** electrocardiogram (ECG) shows changes in cardiac function that reflects changes in emotion
- **blood pressure** is expressed as peak pressure during **systoles** over minimum pressure during **diastoles**; 130/70 mm/Hg is normal; greater than 150/90 is **hypertension**; the device commonly used to measure blood pressure is a **sphygmomanometer**
- **plethysmography** is the measurement of the volume of blood in a body structure (e.g., penis); this is done either with a strain gauge or by measuring the amount of light absorbed by the structure

3. **Invasive Physiological and Pharmacological Methods**

- in most cases, laboratory animals serve as the subjects when invasive procedures are required to directly manipulate or measure the brain

a. **Stereotaxic Surgery** (see Fig. 5.14 in *BIOPSYCHOLOGY;* use *Digital Image Archive Figure CH05F14.BMP)*

- the first step in many invasive biopsychology experiments is stereotaxic surgery; it allows accurate placement of lesions, probes, electrodes, and other devices into the brain
- the method employs a **stereotaxic atlas** and a **stereotaxic instrument** (head holder and electrode holder)
- the reference point is often **bregma** (the point where two main plates of the rat skull naturally fuse together)

b. Lesion Methods (see Fig. 5.15 and Fig. 5.16 in *BIOPSYCHOLOGY;* use *Digital Image Archive Figure CH05F15.BMP* and *CH05F15.BMP)*

- the **aspiration** method is often used to remove cortical tissue
- the **radio-frequency** (high-frequency) electrolytic lesion is the most common subcortical lesion; the tissue is destroyed by the heat of the current
- small **knife cuts** are often used for severing tracts
- **cryogenic blockade** is like a reversible lesion; the tissue is temporarily cooled to the point that all neural activity in the vicinity of the probe stops
- lesions studies must be interpreted with caution; a lesion inevitably damages structures other than the one that the surgeon targeted, and lesions seldom completely remove a structure that is targeted

c. Electrical Stimulation
- the effects of electrical stimulation are often opposite to those of a lesion to the same brain site
- electrical stimulation research is done prior to any lesioning

d. Electrical Recording Methods (see Fig. 5.17 in *BIOPSYCHOLOGY;* use *Digital Image Archive Figure CH05F17.BMP)*

i) intracellular unit recording
- measures changes in the **membrane potential** of a neuron over time; it requires a **microelectrode** positioned **inside a neuron**
- it is next to impossible to record intracellularly in a freely moving animal because it is difficult to keep the microelectrode inside the neuron

ii) extracellular unit recording
- a microelectrode is positioned **near a neuron**
- the signal is a series of spikes; each spike indicates an **action potential** from a nearby neuron; spikes of the same amplitude are assumed to come from the same neuron

iii) multiple-unit recording
- multiple-unit recording provides an indication of the rate of firing of many neurons in the general vicinity of the electrode tip
- an electrode larger than a microelectrode picks up the action potentials from **many nearby neurons**
- the signal is integrated so that the height of the curve indicates the number of action potentials in the vicinity per unit of time

iv) invasive EEG recording
- implanted electrodes are used to record EEG in laboratory animals because scalp electrodes do not allow as clear or finite position recording

e. Pharmacological Methods (see Fig. 5.18 - Fig. 5.21 in *BIOPSYCHOLOGY)*

- routes of drug administration include **IG, IP, IV, SC, IM**
- these peripheral routes all suffer from the fact that many drugs cannot pass the **blood-brain barrier;** this problem can be overcome by administering drug via **intraventricular** cannula or by microinjection of drugs directly into brain tissue
- sometimes, drugs can be injected into the brain that produce chemical lesions that are more selective than electrical lesion might be; for example, **6-hydroxydopamine** (6-OHDA) is a neurotoxin that selectively destroys dopaminergic and noradrenergic neurons in the vicinity of the injection site

i) Measuring the Chemical Activity of the Brain:

- in **2-deoxyglucose autoradiography,** radioactive 2-DG is injected; then the animal performs the behavior of interest
- the animal is immediately killed; its brain is removed and sliced, and the slices are coated with a photographic emulsion
- after a few days in the dark, the areas of the brain that were particularly active during the test activity show up as dark spots of radioactivity
- a technique that allows the measurement of specific neurotransmitters in behaving animals is called *in vivo* **cerebral microdialysis**
- a fine U-shaped tube is inserted into the brain of an animal; its tip is made of a semipermeable dialysis membrane; a solution of artificial cerebrospinal fluid circulates through the tube
- because the tip of the tube is semipermeable, chemicals can continuously move from the brain into the solution in the tube (down a concentration gradient), which can then be removed for later analysis using a **chromatograph**

ii) Locating Neurotransmitters and Receptors in the Brain:

- **immunocytochemistry** begins by injecting **antigens** (foreign proteins) into an animal such that the animal will create and bind **antibodies** to the antigen to remove or destroy it
- antibodies for most of the brain's **peptide neurotransmitters and receptors** have been created; these can be labeled with a dye or radioactive element and then used to identify specific neuroproteins in slices of brain tissue
- *in situ* **hybridization** allows peptides and proteins in the brain to be located; labeled hybrid RNA strands with a base sequence complementary to the mRNA for synthesizing the target neuroprotein; the hybrid RNA binds to the complementary mRNA in the target cells and allows the target neuroprotein's location to be marked

4. Genetic Engineering

a. Gene Knockout Techniques:
- involve the creation of organisms that lack a specific gene; any measurable neural or behavioral anomalies are then noted
- **PROBLEMS:** i) Most behaviors are determined by multiple genes; ii) Eliminating one gene usually alters the expression of other genes; and iii) gene expression is dependent upon experience, which may be altered by the absence of the missing gene

b. Gene Replacement Techniques:
- involves the replacement of one gene with another; useful implications for the treatment of genetically-related diseases
- sometimes, genetic information from a different species is implanted, creating a **transgenic** subject.

Suggested Websites for Lecture 5a:

A Primer for CAT and MRI: *http://www.med.harvard.edu/AANLIB/hms1.html*
> From Dr. Keith Johnston's Whole Brain Atlas, an explanation of CAT and MRI techniques.

The Electroencephalogram (EEG): *http://www.medfak.uu.se/fysiologi/Lectures/EEG.html*
> A great page with basic information about EEGs and evoked potentials, and rudimentary information about the use of EEG in pathological conditions.

***In vivo* Microdialysis:** *http://www.microdialysis.se/techniqu.htm*
> From CMA, a basic description of the technique of in vivo microdialysis, used to measure neurochemical changes in conscious, freely moving animals.

Lecture 5b

BEHAVIORAL RESEARCH METHODS OF BIOPSYCHOLOGY

Outline

1. Neuropsychological Testing
   a. General Tests: The WAIS
   b. General Tests of Language Function
   c. Specific Tests of Memory
   d. Specific Tests of Language
   e. Specific Tests of Frontal Lobe Function

2. Behavioral Methods of Cognitive Neuroscience
   a. Assumption of Constituent Cognitive Processes
   b. Paired Image Subtraction Technique

3. Paradigms of Animal Behavior
   a. Analysis of Species-Common Behaviors
   b. Traditional Conditioning Paradigms
   c. Seminatural Animal Learning Paradigms

4. Conclusion: Converging Operations

Lecture Notes

1. Neuropsychological Testing

- methods used to assess psychological deficits of human patients suspected of having brain damage
- traditionally, a **single neuropsychological test** was administered to a patient; this approach changed in the 1960's to include a **standard battery** of neuropsychological tests; currently, it is most common for a **customized-test-battery** approach to be used

   a. General Tests: The WAIS: (see Table 5.1 in *BIOPSYCHOLOGY*)

- most neuropsychological assessments begin with the **Wechsler Adult Intelligence Scale (WAIS)**
- it has 11 subtests; 6 comprise the **verbal scale** (e.g., digit span, information, similarities); 5 comprise the **performance scale** (e.g., block design, object assembly)
- the **information subtest** and the **digit span test** are memory tests that comprise part of the WAIS; however, these are notoriously bad measures of memory.

   b. General Tests of Language Function

- the WAIS verbal subtests reveal significant language impairments in a variety of ways; if the WAIS was not done, the **token test** is a good initial screening test for language-related deficits; there are 20 tokens of 2 different shapes, 2 different sizes, and 5 different colors; the subject is asked to carry out various acts such as "touch the small blue circle and then the large green square"
- if the token test identifies language deficits, it is followed by a battery of tests of language ability
- a test for the **lateralization of language skills** is also often included when assessing language function
- in the **sodium amytal test**, the anesthetic sodium amytal is injected first into one **carotid artery** and then, many minutes later, into the other; typically, the patient is mute following an injection ipsilateral to the dominant hemisphere for language but makes only a few minor speech errors after an injection contralateral to the dominant hemisphere for language

- in the **dichotic listening test,** three pairs of digits are presented to the subject through headphones; each digit in the pair is presented simultaneously, one to each ear; the subjects are asked to report the six digits that they heard; they do slightly better through the ear contralateral to the hemisphere dominant for language

c. **Specific Tests of Memory**

- if memory deficits are discovered, the neuropsychologist attempts to answer **4 key questions:**

      i) is **short-term** or **long-term** memory affected…or both?
      ii) are the deficits **anterograde** or **retrograde**…or both?
      iii) do the deficits involve **semantic** or **episodic** memory…or both?
      iv) Do the deficits involve **explicit mem**ory or **implicit memory**…or both?

d. **Specific Tests of Language**

- if language deficits are discovered, the neuropsychologist attempts to determine whether the problem is one of **phonology** (understanding the rules for the sounds of language); of **syntax** (the grammar of language); or of **semantics** (the meanings of the language).

e. **Specific Tests of Frontal Lobe Function** (see Fig. 5.22 in *BIOPSYCHOLOGY)*

- the **Wisconsin Card Sorting Test** is often used to assess frontal lobe function
- each card in the deck has 1, 2, 3, or 4 triangles, circles, squares, or crosses that are all red, green, yellow, or blue
- the subject is told to sort the cards into four different piles but is not told on what basis the sorting is to be accomplished; they are told after each card is placed in a pile whether or not it was correctly placed
- at first the patient must learn to sort by color, but once she or he has learned this sorting principle, the correct principle changes without warning to form or number
- patients with **frontal-lobe lesions** adapt poorly to rule changes; they **perseverate** (they continue to respond in a previously correct fashion long after it has become incorrect)

2. **Behavioral Methods of Cognitive Neuroscience** (see Fig. 5.23 in *BIOPSYCHOLOGY)*

a. **assumption of constituent cognitive processes**

- the premise that complex cognitive processes are the **combined activity** of **simple cognitive processes** and that each constituent cognitive process is mediated by neural activity in a particular area of the brain
- **cognitive psychologists, computer scientists**, and **neuroscientists** combine efforts to **model complex cognitive processes**, for clinical as well as artificial intelligence applications

b. **paired-image subtraction techniques**

- a key imaging technique in **cognitive neuroscience research**
- **PET** or **fMRI** images of tasks that differ in only one constituent cognitive process are **compared;** the difference between the two images is viewed as specific to the one constituent cognitive process that was different between the two images
- **signal averaging** is often used to reduce the noise associated with random cerebral events

3.   Animal Behavior Paradigms

    a.   Analysis of Species-Common Behaviors

-   these behaviors are displayed in the same form by virtually all members of a species, of the same sex (e.g., grooming, swimming, nest building, copulating)

-   the **open-field test** provides three measures of emotionality: (1) degree of **inactivity;** (2) **thigmotaxis;** and (3) **defecation**

-   **aggression** and **defense** can be studied by recording encounters between a small male intruder and a colony's dominant (**alpha**) male; **aggression** involves a sideways approach, sideways pushing, piloerection, and biting directed at the back; **defense** involves boxing, rolling over onto the back, biting the face, freezing, and fleeing

-   rat **sexual behavior** is another species-common behavior that is widely studied
-   two common measures of female rat sexual receptivity are (1) **lordosis quotient** (proportion of mounts producing lordosis), and (2) degree of concavity of the back during lordosis
-   male rat behaviors measured include number of **mounts** to **intromission**, number of intromissions to **ejaculation,** and time to reinitiate mounting after ejaculation (the **postejaculatory interval**)

    b.   Traditional Conditioning Paradigms

-   traditional conditioning paradigms play an important role in biopsychology for **three reasons:**

        i) conditioning is a phenomenon of **primary interest** to psychologists;
        ii) conditioning procedures are often used to **train laboratory animals** to perform as required in behavioral experiments; and
        iii) researchers can infer much about the **psychological state** of an animal from its ability to learn and perform various responses

-   there are two kinds of traditional conditioning paradigms:
-

        i) Pavlovian conditioning: in which a neutral stimulus called a **conditional stimulus** (CS; e.g., tone) is paired with an **unconditional stimulus** (US; e.g. meat powder) that elicits an **unconditional response** (UR; e.g. salivation). As the CS becomes associated with the US, it begins to elicit a response on its own which is referred to as a conditional response (CR). The CR is usually similar to the UR, but this is not always the case.
        ii) Operant Conditioning: in which the rate of a particular response is increased by **reinforcement** or decreased by **punishment.**

    c.   Seminatural Animal Learning Paradigms (see Fig. 5.24 in *BIOPSYCHOLOGY;* use *Digital Image Archive Figure CH05F25.BMP)*

-   **ethoexperimental** animal learning paradigms are controlled laboratory paradigms for studying forms of learning that are assumed to occur in the rat's natural environment; the following are four examples:

    i) Conditioned Taste Aversion:
-   the most influential ethoexperimental learning paradigm; rats and many other animals learn the relation between a new taste and subsequent gastrointestinal distress in one trial and subsequently avoid the novel taste

- taste aversion conditioning experiments in the 1960s challenged three widely held views of learning that had grown out of the study of the traditional conditioning paradigms:

> 1) the view that learning is a gradual **step-by-step process** by showing that it could occur reliably in one trial;
> 2) the view that **temporal contiguity** is necessary for learning by showing that conditioning occurred even when the taste and distress were separated by several hours; and
> 3) the view that associations between any two stimuli are equally easy to learn (the **principle of equipotentiality**) by showing that rats could learn the relation between gastrointestinal distress and a taste, but not a light

ii) Radial-Arm Maze:
- is used to study foraging behavior in the laboratory
- foraging in the wild is complex; the rat must learn where food is likely to be, but not to immediately revisit a stripped site
- in the radial-arm maze rats quickly learn to go directly to the arms that are baited with food each day, but they rarely visit the same arm twice on a given trial

iii) Morris Water Maze:
- is another laboratory paradigm used to study rat spatial ability; the Morris water maze is a large tub of milky water; to get out of the water, rats must learn to swim to a slightly submerged (invisible) goal platform
- rats learn to do this very quickly, even when they are placed in the water at a different position on each trial; they use external room cues to guide them
- it is interesting to look at their search strategies when the platform has been moved to a new location

iv) Conditioned Defensive Burying:
- based on observation that rats exposed to an inanimate object that has been the source of a single aversive stimulus (e.g., a shock, a bad odor, an air blast, or a flash) will often bury it
- they bury it by facing it and spraying bedding or sand at it with their head and forelegs
- it has been used to study antianxiety drug effects; antianxiety drugs reduce conditioned defensive burying at low doses

4.   Conclusion: Converging Operations

- you have now learned about many research methods used by biopsychologists; they all have strengths, but they all have weaknesses
- the key to scientific progress lies in **converging operations** (bringing several methods to bear on the same problem so that each compensates for the shortcomings of the others)

Suggested Websites for Lecture 5b:

The Wechsler Intelligence Scales: *http://www.findarticles.com/cf_dls/g2601/0014/2601001473/p1/article.jhtml*
> A page focusing on the Wechsler Intelligence scales, including a history of the WAIS, its subscales, and the WISC. See the Pros and Cons section for high (and low) points of these scales.

Virtual Operant Conditioning: *http://cayo.net/psy/demolist.html*
> The website for Crofter Publishing, where you can download the demo software for OpRat, a program that allows students to study the operant behavior of a virtual rat. Full version of the software is only available commercially.

Why Study Animal Behavior? *http://www.animalbehavior.org/ABS/Education/valueofanimalbehavior.html*
> From Dr. Charles Snowdon, a past president of the Animal Behavior Society; thoughtful essay on the value of basic and applied animal research.

IM-At-A-Glance. Chapter 6: The Visual System:
From Your Eyes to Your Cortex

Detailed Outline	Print Supplements	Media Supplements	Professor's Notes
Chapter 6. The Visual System: From Your Eyes to Your Cortex, pp. 132-160 6.1 Light Enters the Eye and Reaches the Retina 6.2 The Retina and Transduction of Light into Neural Signals 6.3 From Retina to Primary Visual Cortex 6.4 Seeing Edges 6.5 Seeing Color	**Instructor's Manual for** *BIOPSYCHOLOGY,* *Lecture 6a and* *Lecture 6b* **Test Bank for** *BIOPSYCHOLOGY,* *Chapter 6* **Study Guide for** *BIOPSYCHOLOGY,* *Chapter 6* **Transparencies for Physiological Psychology:** *V. Sensation & Perception:* *The Visual System*	***Beyond the Brain & Behavior CD for* BIOPSYCHOLOGY:** *Surface Interpolation Module;* *Contrast Enhancement Module;* *Practice Tests for Chapter 6* *Hard Copy for Chapter 6* *Electronic Flashcards for Chapter 6* **Digital Image Archive, Powerpoint Presentation and Bitmap Images for* BIOPSYCHOLOGY:** *Chapter 7* ***BIOLOGICAL PSYCHOLOGY VIDEO:*** *Segment 7.* The Visual System	

Lecture 6a

THE VISUAL SYSTEM: EYE TO CORTEX

Outline

1. The Eyes
   a. Structure
   b. Accommodation
   c. Binocular Disparity

2. The Retina
   a. Structure
   b. Completion
   c. Cone & Rod Vision
   d. Eye Movements

3. Visual Transduction by Rhodopsin

4. From Retina to Primary Visual Cortex

Lecture Notes

1. **The Eyes:** (see Fig. 6.2 – Fig. 6.4 in *BIOPSYCHOLOGY;* use *Digital Image Archive Figure CH07F03.BMP;* use **Segment 7.** *The Visual System* of the **BIOLOGICAL PSYCHOLOGY** video)

   - vision is the most studied of the senses

   a. Structure:

   - review the major structures of the eye
   - note that the size of the **pupils** is a compromise between **sensitivity** and **acuity**

   b. Accommodation:

   - **ciliary muscles** adjust the lenses to focus visual images sharply on each retina, regardless of the distance of the image from the eyes; this focusing is called **accommodation**
   - when we look at something near, the ciliary muscles contract, tension on the lenses is reduced, and they become more cylindrical
   - when we look at a distant object, the muscles relax, tension on the lens is increased, and the lenses flatten

   c. Binocular Disparity

   - unlike most vertebrates, most mammals have **two eyes** on the **front of their heads,** rather than one on each side; this cuts down the field of view, but it insures that most of what is seen is seen through both eyes
   - because each eye sees things from a slightly different perspective, there is a difference in the two retinal images; this **binocular disparity** is greater for closer things; the degree of binocular disparity associated with a particular visual stimulus helps the brain create a **3-dimensional perception** from two 2-dimensional retinal images thus depth perception is achieved

2. The Retina (see Fig. 6.5 – Fig. 6.9 in *BIOPSYCHOLOGY;* use **The Cornsweet Illusion** module from **Beyond the Brain & Behavior CD** for *BIOPSYCHOLOGY;* use *Digital Image Archive Figure CH07F04.BMP, CH07F07.BMP* and *CH07F09.BMP;* use **Segment 7.** *The Visual System* of the **BIOLOGICAL PSYCHOLOGY** video)

a. **Structure**

- **five layers:** receptor layer; horizontal cell layer; bipolar layer; amacrine cell layer; and retinal ganglion cell layer
- the receptor layer is the **farthest from light;** therefore, incoming light is distorted by four layers of neurons before reaching the receptors
- the **fovea** is a pit about 330 μ in diameter; it is the only part of the retina capable of mediating **high-acuity vision.** This is due, in part, to the fact that axons of the retinal ganglion cells are thinnest over the fovea and light is distorted less before reaching the layer of receptors. The fovea is roughly in the center of your field of vision, which is why you tend to hold tasks that require a high degree of acuity (e.g., threading a needle) in the center of your visual field.
- the **optic disk** is where the axons of retinal ganglion cells penetrate the retina and exit the eye; the optic disk has no receptors thus creating a **blind spot**

b. **Completion**

- we all have a **blind spot** at the **optic disk,** due to the exit of axons from the retinal ganglion cells
- we are normally unaware of our blind spots, even when looking through one stationary eye, because of **completion;** the visual system is able to use visual information gathered from receptors around the optic disk to "complete" the visual image
- completion illustrates the **creativity** of the visual system

c. **Cone & Rod Vision**

- in a sense, each of us has two visual systems; the **photopic** system functions in lighted conditions; the **scotopic** system functions in dim light
- **cones** mediate photopic vision; **rods** mediate scotopic vision; this is called the **duplexity theory of vision**
- the photopic system mediates **high-acuity** vision; the scotopic system mediates **low-acuity** vision
- the photopic system has **low sensitivity** with few receptors' information combined at the next cell level **(low convergence)**
- the scotopic system has **high sensitivity** with many receptors converging on ganglion cells **(high convergence)**
- only cones are in the fovea; rods predominate in the periphery

d. **Eye Movements**

- our eyes are in continual motion; they make a series of **fixations** (about 3 per second) connected by **saccades** (rapid movements between fixations)
- eye movements keep the visual image in continual motion on the retina; the importance of this movement is illustrated by the fact that **stabilized retinal images** disappear; most visual system neurons respond to **change,** not to steady input
- what we perceive at any instance is the sum of the input that has been received during the last few fixations; this **temporal integration** of retinal images explains why our visual images are detailed, colored, and wide-angled, despite the small size of the fovea; it also explains why things don't disappear when we blink

3. **Visual Transduction by Rhodopsin** (see Fig. 6.12 in *BIOPSYCHOLOGY;* use *Digital Image Archive Figure CH07F11.BMP;* use **Segment 7.** *The Visual System* of the **BIOLOGICAL PSYCHOLOGY video)**

    -   **transduction** is the conversion of one form of energy to another; the first step in visual transduction is conversion of light to neural signals by the rods and cones
    -   transduction by rods is well understood; there is a pink substance in rods called **rhodopsin**; light is absorbed by **rhodopsin**, and this **bleaches** it (removes its color); this bleaching occurs because **retinal** and **opsin**, the two components of rhodopsin, separate in light
    -   this bleaching reaction **hyperpolarizes** the rods, thus the bleaching reaction transduces light to a cascade of intracellular events resulting in a neural signal
    -   when rhodopsin is totally bleached by intense light, rods lose their ability to absorb light and transduce; however, in the dark, retinal and opsin are reunited, and rhodopsin regains its color and its ability to absorb light and transduce
    -   strong evidence that the absorption of light by rhodopsin is the first step in scotopic vision is the correspondence between rhodopsin's **absorption spectrum** and the scotopic **spectral sensitivity curve**
    -   rhodopsin is a G-protein linked receptor that responds to light by initiating a cascade of intracellular chemical events
    -   **cyclic GMP** is an intracellular chemical that keeps Na+ channels partly open when rods are in darkness; rods are thus slightly **depolarized**
    -   bleaching rods via exposure to light results in an intracellular cascade of events that deactivates cyclic GMP, closing Na+ channels, which **hyperpolarizes** the rod and reduces the release of glutamate
    -   rods thus transmit signals through the neural system via inhibition

4. **From Retina to Primary Visual Cortex** (see Fig. 6.13 in *BIOPSYCHOLOGY;* use *Digital Image Archive Figure CH07F12.BMP;* use **Segment 7.** *The Visual System* of the **BIOLOGICAL PSYCHOLOGY video)**

    -   this is called the **retina-geniculate-striate pathway**
    -   the primary visual cortex is called **striate cortex** after the stripe seen in a Nissl-stained cross section of **lower layer IV**; the stripe is composed of the terminals of axons from the lateral geniculate nuclei
    -   the retinal ganglion cell axons from the **nasal hemiretinas** decussate via the **optic chiasm** (they are contralateral); those from the **temporal hemiretinas** remain **ipsilateral** providing redundancy for the system
    -   the most important feature of visual cortex organization is its **retinotopic** layout; the surface of the visual cortex is a **map** of the retina; demonstrated when Dobelle et al. (1974) stimulated the visual cortex of patients who were blind from peripheral damage with an array of electrodes; the patients saw a pattern of light that corresponded to the pattern on the cortex of electrodes that were simultaneously activated
    -   the **retina-geniculate-striate system** includes two largely independent channels: the **P pathway** and the **M pathway**

        1) **Parvocellular layers** (P layers) are found in the top four layers of each lateral geniculate nucleus (LGN) and are composed of small body neurons (parvo means "small"); they are responsive to color, fine detail patterns, and react to slow or stationary objects
        2) **Magnocellular layers** (M layers) are found in the bottom two layers of the LGN, composed of large body neurons (magno means "large"), and are responsive to rods and movement

Suggest Websites for Lecture 6a:

First Stages of Vision: *http://www.accessexcellence.org/AE/AEC/CC/vision_background.html*
> From Genentech's Access Excellence site, a comprehensive yet accessible review of the anatomy and physiology of the eye.

Retinal Implants: *http://rleweb.mit.edu/retina/*
> A joint project of Harvard and MIT, one of several groups world-wide that are striving to perfect electronic retinal prostheses for people suffering from degenerative retinal diseases.

Visual Prostheses: *http://www.artificialvision.com/vision/index.html*
> From the Dobelle Institute, information about cutting edge visual prostheses…a blind man sees!

Lecture 6b

THE PERCEPTION OF CONTRAST AND COLOR

Outline

1.   Contrast: The Perception of Edges
     a. Lateral Inhibition: The Physiological Basis of Contrast Enhancement

2.   Brightness-Contrast Detectors in the Mammalian Visual System
     a. Mapping Receptive Fields
     b. Receptive Fields of Neurons in the Retina-Geniculate-Striate Pathway
     c. Simple Cortical Cells
     d. Complex Cortical Cells
     e. Hubel and Wiesel's Model of Striate-Cortex Organization

3.   Seeing Color
     a. Component Theory
     b. Opponent Process Theory
     c. Color Constancy

Lecture Notes

1.   **Contrast: The Perception of Edges** (see Fig. 6.14 and Fig. 6.15 in *BIOPSYCHOLOGY;* use **The Contrast Enhancement** module from **Beyond the Brain & Behavior CD for** *BIOPSYCHOLOGY;* use *Digital Image Archive Figure CH07F13.BMP* and *CH07F14.BMP;* use **Segment 7.** *The Visual System* of the **BIOLOGICAL PSYCHOLOGY video)**

     - edges are the most important stimuli in our visual world; they define the position and extent of things
     - edge perception is the perception of a contrast between two adjacent areas of the visual field; this lecture will focus on how the visual system controls **brightness contrast**
     - the perception of edges is so important that there is a mechanism in the visual system that enhances our perception of brightness contrast; this is called **contrast enhancement**; thus what we see is even better than the physical reality
     - the **Mach bands** illusion is the result of contrast enhancement; in it, light areas that are near the border with a dark region appear lighter than they really are, and the area of the dark region that lies along this border looks darker than it really is

     a.   **Lateral Inhibition: The Physiological Basis of Contrast Enhancement**

     - the mechanisms of contrast enhancement were studied in the eye of the horseshoe crab because of its simplicity; it is a simple compound eye, with each of its individual receptors (**ommatidia**) connected by a lateral neural network (the **lateral plexus**)
     - when an ommatidium is activated, it inhibits its neighbors via the lateral plexus; contrast enhancement occurs because receptors near an edge on the dimmer side receive **more lateral inhibition** than receptors on the dimmer side further away from the edge while receptors near the edge on the brighter side receive **less lateral inhibition** than the receptors on the brighter further away from the edge

2.   **Brightness-Contrast Detectors in the Mammalian Visual System:** (see Fig. 6.16 - Fig. 6.22 in *BIOPSYCHOLOGY;* use *Digital Image Archive Figure CH07F15.BM - CH07F21.BMP;* use **Segment 7.** *The Visual System* of the **BIOLOGICAL PSYCHOLOGY video)**

     a.   **Mapping Receptive Fields**

     - in the late 1950s, Hubel and Wiesel developed a method that became the standard method for studying visual system neurons

- visual stimuli are presented on a screen in front of a **curarized** subject (usually a cat or a monkey); the image is artificially focused on the retina by an adjustable lens in front of the eye (because the **ciliary muscles** are curarized)
- once an extracellular electrode is positioned in the neural structure of interest so that it is recording the action potentials of only one neuron, the neuron's receptive field is mapped; the **receptive field** of a neuron is the area of the visual field within which **appropriate visual stimuli** can influence the firing of that neuron
- once the receptive field is defined, the task is to discover what particular stimuli presented within the field are most effective in changing the cell's firing

b. Receptive Fields of Neurons in the Retina-Geniculate-Striate Pathway

- most **retinal ganglion cells, lateral geniculate nucleus neurons**, and the neurons in **lower layer IV** of the striate cortex have similar receptive fields: they are smaller in the foveal area; they are circular; they are monocular; and they have both an excitatory and an inhibitory area separated by a circular boundary.
- neurons in these regions have **2 patterns of responding**: 1) **on firing**; or (2) inhibition followed by **off firing**
- the most effective way to influence the firing of these neurons is to fully illuminate only the **"on area"** or the **"off area"** of its receptive field; if one light is shone in the "on area" and one is simultaneously shone in the "off area", their effects cancel one another out by lateral inhibition; these neurons respond little to diffuse light
- in effect, many neurons of the retina-geniculate-striate pathway respond to **brightness contrast** between the centers and peripheries of their visual fields

c. Simple Cortical Cells

- simple cortical cells in the striate cortex have receptive fields like those that were just described, except that the two areas of the receptive fields are divided by straight lines
- these cells respond best to bars or edges of light in a particular location in the receptive field and in a particular orientation (e.g., 45°)
- all simple cells are **monocular**

d. Complex Cortical Cells

- most of the cells in the striate cortex are **complex cells**; they are more numerous but are like simple cells in that they respond best to straight-line stimuli in a particular orientation; they are not responsive to diffuse light
- complex cells are unlike simple cells in that the position of the stimulus within the receptive field does not matter; the cell responds to the appropriate stimulus no matter where it is in its large receptive field
- over half of the complex cells are **binocular**, and about half of those that are binocular display **ocular dominance**

e. Hubel and Wiesel's Model of Striate-Cortex Organization

- when you record from visual cortex using **vertical electrode passes,** you find: (1) cells with receptive fields in the same part of the receptive field, (2) simple and complex, cells that all prefer the same orientation, and (3) binocular complex cells that are all dominated by the same eye (if they display ocular dominance)
- when you record from visual cortex using **horizontal electrode passes** you find: (1) receptive field location shifts slightly with each electrode advance, (2) orientation preference shifts slightly with each electrode advance, (3) ocular dominance periodically shifts to the other eye with electrode advances
- **ocular dominance columns** can be visualized by injecting a large dose of **radioactive amino acid** in one eye, waiting several days, and then subjecting the cortex to **autoradiography**; ocular dominance columns are clearly visible in lower layer IV as alternating patches of radioactivity and nonradioactivity

- columns of vertical-line-preferring neurons have been visualized by injecting **radioactive 2-DG** and then moving vertical stripes back and forth in front of the animal for 45 min.; the subjects were then immediately killed and their brains sectioned; columns of radioactivity were visible through all layers of striate cortex except lower layer IV

2. **Seeing Color:** (see Fig. 6.26 - Fig. 6.29 in *BIOPSYCHOLOGY;* use *Digital Image Archive Figure CH07F26.BM* and *CH07F28.BMP;* use **Segment 7.** *The Visual System* of the **BIOLOGICAL PSYCHOLOGY video)**

    a. **Component Theory**

    - also called **trichromatic theory**; first proposed in 1802 by Thomas Young & refined by von Helmholtz in 1852
    - component processing occurs at the **receptor level**
    - KEY IDEA: one of **three different photopigments** coats each cone; each photopigment reacts optimally to a particular part of the spectrum of electromagnetic energy; the **ratio of cones** activated at a particular part of the color spectrum creates a summed stimulus and thus color differentiation

    b. **Opponent Process Theory**

    - first proposed by Hering in 1878
    - opponent processing occurs at all levels of the visual system beyond the receptors
    - KEY IDEA: **three classes of cells:** one that becomes more active to red and less active to green; one that becomes more active to blue and less active to yellow; and one that becomes more active to bright and less active to dark areas.
    - with regards to color vision, red-green and blue-yellow opponent cells fire in response to input from cones; when red cells are "on" one cannot see green and when yellow cells are "on" one cannot see blue

    c. **Color Constancy**

    - this is the tendency for an object to be perceived as the same color despite major changes in wavelengths of light that it reflects
    - perception of color constancy allows objects to be distinguished in a memorable way
    - Land demonstrated in his 1977 experiments that the color of objects is not a simple relationship with the wavelength being reflected but depends partly on the light reflected by surfaces surrounding the objects
    - Land's **retinex theory of color vision** follows the premise that the color of an object is determined by its reflectance and the visual system calculates the reflectance of surfaces by comparing the ability of a surface to absorb light in the three bandwidths corresponding to the three classes of cones
    - **dual-opponent cells** provide the means to analyze contrast between wavelengths reflected by adjacent areas of their receptive fields

Suggested Websites for Lecture 7b:

On-Line Illusions and other Visual Phenomena: *http://faculty.washington.edu/chudler/chvision.html*
A great set of exercises from Dr. Eric Chudler's site at the University of Washington; check out the demonstrations of blind spots, negative after-images, dark adaptation...lots more!

Color Vision: *http://www.hhmi.org/senses/b110.html*
From the Howard Hughes Medical Institute's *Hearing, Seeing and Smelling* site, a very good review of the physiological basis of color vision.

Animation of Receptive Fields: *http://psychlab1.hanover.edu/Classes/Neuro/Internet/Receptive Fields/*
From Dr. John Krantz at Hanover College, an animation illustrating the receptive fields of the retina.

IM-At-A-Glance. Chapter 7: Mechanisms of Perception, Conscious Awareness, & Attention: How You Know the World

Detailed Outline	Print Supplements	Media Supplements	Professor's Notes
Chapter 7. Mechanisms of Perception, Conscious Awareness, & Attention: How You Know the World pp. 161-193 7.1 Principles of Sensory System Organization 7.2 Cortical Mechanisms of Vision 7.3 Audition 7.4 Somatosensation: Touch & Pain 7.5 The Chemical Senses: Smell & Taste 7.6 Selective Attention	**Instructor's Manual for** *BIOPSYCHOLOGY,* *Lecture 7a and Lecture 7b* **Test Bank for** *BIOPSYCHOLOGY,* *Chapter 7* **Study Guide for** *BIOPSYCHOLOGY,* *Chapter 7* **Transparencies for Physiological Psychology:** *V. Sensation & Perception*	*Beyond the Brain &* *Behavior CD for* **BIOPSYCHOLOGY:** *Change Blindness Module ; Investigating Olfaction: The Nose Knows Module* *Practice Tests for Chapter 7* *Hard Copy for Chapter 7* *Electronic Flashcards for Chapter 7* **Digital Image Archive, Powerpoint Presentation and Bitmap Images for** *BIOPSYCHOLOGY:* *Chapter 8*	

Lecture 7a

CORTICAL MECHANISMS OF VISION AND AUDITION

Outline

1. General Concepts
   a. The Traditional Hierarchical Sensory-System Model
   b. Sensation and Perception
   c. Hierarchical Organization

2. Cortical Mechanisms of Vision
   a. Scotomas and Blindsight
   b. Completion
   c. Secondary Visual Cortex and Association Cortex
   d. Visual Agnosia

3. Auditory System
   a. The Ear
   b. Auditory Projections
   c. Auditory Cortex
   d. Sound Localization

Lecture Notes

1. **General Concepts** (see Fig. 7.1 and Fig. 7.2 in *BIOPSYCHOLOGY;* use *Digital Image Archive Figure CH08F02.BMP)*

   - we have discussed the visual system from the eye to the striate (primary visual) cortex
   - this lecture will focus on cortical mechanisms involved in the processing of visual and auditory information

   a. **The Traditional Hierarchical Sensory-System Model**

   - traditionally, sensory-system organization has been viewed according to the following model: input flows from receptors to thalamus, to primary sensory cortex, to secondary sensory cortex, and finally to association cortex
   - **primary sensory cortex** is cortex that receives input directly from **thalamic sensory relay nuclei;** the **secondary sensory cortex** of a sensory system receives input primarily from the primary sensory cortex of that system; **association cortex** is cortex that receives input from more than one sensory system
   - the major feature of the traditional sensory-system model is its serial and hierarchical organization; a **hierarchical system** is any system with components that can be assigned to ranks
   - sensory systems are thought to be hierarchical in two ways: (1) sensory information is thought to flow through brain structures in order of their **increasing neuroanatomical complexity,** and (2) sensation is thought to be less complex than perception
   - the neuroanatomical hierarchy is thought to be related to the functional hierarchy; **perception** is often assumed to be a function of **cortical structures**

   b. **Sensation and Perception**

   - **sensation** refers to the simple process of detecting the presence of a stimulus; **perception** refers to the complex process of integrating, recognizing, and interpreting complex patterns of sensations
   - the need for this distinction is illustrated by the case of Dr. P, the man who mistook his wife for a hat; he had severe visual perception problems in the absence of disturbances in visual sensation

c. The Current Parallel, Functionally Segregated Hierarchical Model of Sensory-System Organization

- it is now clear that sensory systems are characterized by a parallel, functionally segregated, hierarchical organization:

Parallel: sensory systems are organized so that information flows between different structures simultaneously along multiple pathways
Functionally Segregated: sensory systems are organized so that different parts of the various structures specialize in different kinds of analysis.
Hierarchical: as noted, information flows through brain structures in order of their increasing neuroanatomical and functional complexity.

The Critical Question: If different types of information are processed in different specialized zones that are found in different structures connected by multiple pathways, how are complex stimuli perceived as an integrated whole? This is known as the **binding problem.**

2. **Cortical Mechanisms of Vision** (see Fig. 7.3 - Fig. 7.11 in *BIOPSYCHOLOGY;* use *Digital Image Archive Figure CH08F03.BMP, Figure CH08F05.BMP,* and *CH08F09.BMP)*

- the occipital cortex and large parts of parietal and temporal lobe cortex is **visual cortex**
- **primary visual cortex** is located in the occipital lobe; **secondary visual cortex** is located in the **prestriate cortex** (surrounds primary visual cortex) and the **inferotemporal cortex;** and most of visual association cortex is **posterior parietal cortex.**

a. Scotomas and Blindsight

- individuals with damage to primary visual cortex have **scotomas** or areas of blindness in the corresponding areas of the visual field; scotomas are plotted by **perimetry**
- amazingly, when forced to guess, some brain-damaged patients can respond to stimuli in their scotomas (e.g., can grab a moving object or guess the direction of its movement), all the while claiming to see nothing; this is called **blindsight**
- blindsight is thought to be mediated by visual pathways that are not part of the retina-geniculate-striate system; for example, one hypothesis is that the retina-geniculate-striate system mediates pattern and color perception, whereas a system involving the **superior colliculus** and the **pulvinar nucleus** of the thalamus mediates the detection and localization of objects in space
- this phenomenon emphasizes that **parallel models** (multiple-path models), rather than **serial models** (single-path models), are needed to explain many perceptual phenomena

b. Completion

- many patients with large scotomas are unaware of them; for example, patients with the complete destruction of the left striate cortex cannot detect stimuli in their right visual fields (they are **hemianopic**), yet when they stare at a face, or even half a face that falls entirely in their left visual field, they report seeing an entire face
- this phenomenon is called **completion**

c. Secondary Visual Cortex and Association Cortices

- visual information is believed to flow along **two anatomically** and **functionally distinct pathways:**

i) a **dorsal stream,** with information flowing from primary visual cortex through the dorsal prestriate secondary visual cortex to association cortex in the posterior parietal region; and
ii) a **ventral stream,** with information flowing from primary visual cortex through the ventral prestriate secondary visual cortex to association cortex in the posterior parietal region

- traditionally, the dorsal stream was believed to be involved in the perception of where object are (**a where** system), while the ventral stream was believed to be involved in the recognition of that object (a **what** system)
- more recently, Milner & Goodale (1993) have proposed that the dorsal stream is actually involved in directing behavioral interactions with objects (which would include, but not be restricted to, analyses of where objects are; a **behavioral control** path), while the ventral stream is responsible for the conscious recognition of objects (a **conscious perception** path).

d. Visual Agnosia

- **agnosia** is a failure to recognize that is not attributable to a simple sensory deficit, or to motor, verbal, or intellectual impairment (gnosis means "to know"); the case of Dr. P., the man who mistook his wife for a hat, is a classic example of **visual agnosia**
- **prosopagnosia**, the inability to recognize faces, is the most interesting and most common form of visual agnosia; prosopagnosics can readily recognize objects (chairs, tables, hats), but they have extreme difficulty telling one face from another; a prosopagnosic may even fail to recognize her or his own face in a mirror
- Tranel and Damasio (1985) showed that despite a lack of conscious recognition for familiar faces, prosopagnosics show **skin conductance changes** indicating a **recognition** of the faces at **subconscious levels**
- the existence of prosopagnosia has led to the view that there is a special area in the brain for the recognition of faces and that it is damaged in prosopagnosics; the finding of neurons in the inferotemporal cortices of monkeys and sheep that appear to respond only to conspecific faces supports this view
- however, reports that a bird watcher and a farmer who suffered from prosopagnosia also lost their ability to recognize specific species of birds and specific cows, respectively, suggests that **prosopagnosia may not be specific to faces;** prosopagnosics may have difficulty distinguishing between visually similar members of complex classes of visual stimuli, of which faces are simply the most obvious class

3. **Auditory System** (see Fig. 7.12 - Fig. 7.16 in *BIOPSYCHOLOGY;* use *Digital Image Archive Figure CH08F13.BMP, Figure CH08F14.BMP,* and *CH08F15.BMP)*

a. The Ear

- vibrations in the air are transmitted through the **tympanic membrane** (ear drum), **ossicles** (three small bones), and **oval window** into the fluid of the cochlea
- the vibrations bend the **organ of Corti** and excite **hair cells** in the **basilar membrane**
- the organization of the organ of Corti is **tonotopic**; higher frequencies excite receptors closer to the oval **window**, thus with exposure to noise as well as decrements due to age, damage to the high frequency receptors occurs first

b. Auditory Projections

- unlike the visual system, there is no one major auditory projection
- **hair cells** synapse on neurons whose axons enter the **metencephalon** and synapse in the ipsilateral **cochlear nucleus**
- from the cochlear nucleus some fibers project to the nearby **superior olives**, which projects to the **inferior colliculus** via the **lateral lemniscus**
- from the inferior colliculus, fibers ascend to the **medial geniculate nucleus** of the thalamus; and from there, fibers ascend to the primary auditory cortex in the lateral fissure
- the projections from each ear are bilateral

c. **Auditory Cortex**

- the auditory cortex located in the **lateral** fissure that separates the temporal and frontal lobes
- it is **tonotopically** organized
- in addition, it is organized into **functional columns** such that neurons in a given column all respond maximally to tones in the same frequency range
- bilateral lesions of auditory cortex do not cause deafness, even if the lesions include secondary auditory cortex
- humans with extensive auditory cortex damage often have difficulty localizing brief stimuli or recognizing rapid complex sequences of sounds

d. **Sound Localization**

- the **superior olives** play a role in sound localization; the **medial superior olives** contain neurons that are sensitive to differences in the time of arrival of a sound at the two ears; the **lateral superior olives** contain neurons that are sensitive to differences in the amplitude of a sound at the two ears
- the layers of the **superior colliculus** that receive input from the superior olives are topographically organized
- much of the research on sound localization has focused on the **barn owl** because of its amazing ability to localize sounds (it hunts mice by their rustling sounds as they move in the dark)

Suggested Websites for Lecture 7a:

Localizing sound: *http://www.hhmi.org/senses/c210.html*
From the Howard Hughes Medical Institute's *Our Precious Senses* site, a look at the extraordinary ability of barn owls to localize sounds.

Central Visual Pathways: *http://thalamus.wustl.edu/course/cenvis.html*
From the Washington University School of Medicine, information about the organization of the visual system from the retina to higher-order visual cortex; includes information on the thalamus, primary visual cortex and ocular dominance columns, and the M- and P-pathways for visual information.

The Virtual Ear: *http://ctl.augie.edu/perry/ear/hearmech.htm*
From Perry Hanavan at Augustana College, a great collection of links to sites related to all parts of the auditory system, from the ear to auditory cortex.

Lecture 7b

**THE SOMATOSENSORY SYSTEM, THE CHEMICAL SENSES, AND
A GENERAL MODEL OF SENSORY SYSTEM ORGANIZATION**

Outline

1. Organization of the Somatosensory System
   a. The Somatosensory Subsystems
   b. Cutaneous Receptors
   c. The Two Ascending Pathways

2. Somatosensory Cortex

3. Pain and the Descending Analgesia Circuit

4. Smell and Taste
   a. The Olfactory System
   b. The Gustatory System

5. Selective Attention

Lecture Notes

1. **Organization of the Somatosensory System** (see Fig. 7.17 – Fig. 7.20 in *BIOPSYCHOLOGY;* use
   Digital Image Archive Figure CH03F19.BMP , CH08F17.BMP - CH08F20.BMP)

   a. **Somatosensation and the Somatosensory Subsystems**

   - the somatosensory system comprises three subsystems: (1) an **exteroceptive** cutaneous system, (2) a
     proprioception system (monitors body position), and (3) an **interoceptive** system (monitors
     conditions within the body such as blood pressure)
   - we are going to focus on the exteroceptive cutaneous subsystem, which in turn comprises three
     somewhat distinct subsystems, which respond to: (1) **mechanical stimulation** of the skin (that is to
     touch), (2) **thermal stimulation** (temperature), and (3) **nociceptive stimuli** (surface pain)

   b. **Cutaneous Receptors and Dermatomes**

   - there are seven kinds of cutaneous; for example there are (1) **free nerve endings**, which provide
     signals about pain and temperature; (2) **Pacinian corpuscles** which are deep fast-adapting touch
     receptors; (3) **Merkel receptors**, and (4) **Ruffini corpuscles**, which are slow-adapting touch receptors
   - the axons carrying sensory information from cutaneous receptors gather together in nerves and enter
     the spinal cord via the **dorsal roots**
   - the area of the body that is innervated by the left and right dorsal roots of a given segment of the
     spinal cord is called a **dermatome** ("skin slice"); the overlap between adjacent dermatomes means
     that destruction of a single dorsal root does not produce complete somatosensory loss

   c. **The Two Ascending Pathways**

   i) **The Dorsal-Column Medial-Lemniscus System**: *(use Digital Image Archive Figure CH08F19.BMP)*

   - the dorsal-column medial-lemniscus system carries information about **touch** and **proprioception** to
     the cortex; the axons of receptors in the skin enter the spinal cord and ascend in the ipsilateral dorsal
     columns to the **dorsal column nuclei**, the axons of dorsal-column-nuclei cells decussate and ascend in
     the **medial lemniscus** to the **ventral posterior nucleus** (VPN); the axons of VPN cells ascend to the
     somatosensory cortex
   - axons from the toes that ascend in the dorsal columns are the longest in the body

ii) **The Anterolateral System:**

- the other ascending somatosensory pathway
- the anterolateral system carries some crude information about touch, but its primary function is to mediate the perception of **pain** and **temperature**
- axons in the anterolateral system synapse as soon as they enter the cord; the second-order axons **decussate immediately** and ascend in one of three different anterolateral pathways: 1) the **spinothalamic tract,** which projects to the ventral posterior nucleus of the thalamus; 2) the **spinoreticular tract,** which projects to the reticular formation and then to the **parafascicular** and **intralaminar nuclei of the thalamus**; and 3) the **spinotectal tract,** which projects to the mesencephalic **tectum**
- Mark and his colleagues found that lesions to the VP thalamus produce a loss of somatosensation and sharp pain perception, while lesions to the parafascicular and intralaminar nuclei of the thalamus reduced perception of chronic pain without disrupting cutaneous sensitivity.

2. **Somatosensory Cortex:** (see Fig. 7.21 and Fig. 7.22 in *BIOPSYCHOLOGY;* use *Digital Image Archive Figure CH08F21.BMP)*

- the various thalamic nuclei receiving somatosensory information project to: (1) primary somatosensory cortex (**SI**) in the **postcentral gyrus,** (2) secondary somatosensory cortex (**SII**), which is ventral to SI, and (3) to the **posterior parietal cortex**
- the primary somatosensory cortex is organized somatotopically; it is known as the **somatosensory homunculus**; studies by Kaas and others have shown that instead of one homunculus (as indicated by the classic early studies of Penfield), primary somatosensory cortex comprises **four parallel somatotopically organized strips**, each sensitive to a different kind of somatosensory input
- cortical lesions to primary somatosensory cortex have only **minor effects on tactual sensitivity**--mainly on the sensitivity of the hands
- large lesions to parietal cortex occasionally produce **somatosensory agnosias**; for example, **astereognosia,** is the loss of the ability to recognize objects by touch in the absence of defects in somatosensation (**stereognosis** is the ability to identify an object by touch), and **asomatognosia** is a loss of the ability to recognize parts of one's own body (e.g., the case of Aunt Betty; described in chapter 7 of BIOPSYCHOLOGY)

3. **Pain and the Descending Analgesia Circuit** (see Fig. 7.23 and Fig. 7.24 in *BIOPSYCHOLOGY;* use *Digital Image Archive Figure CH08F24.BMP)*

- although most people think of pain as bad, it is very adaptive; cases of **congenital pain insensitivity** rarely survive their teens (e.g., they suffer many burns, lacerations, and joint problems, and any internal disorder such as appendicitis is lethal (see the case of Miss C. in Chapter 7of BIOPSYCHOLOGY)
- the cortical representation of pain is very complex; using PET, researchers have found that the **anterior cingulate cortex** has been consistently implicated in cortical perception of pain; however it appears that this activation is more related to **emotional responses** to pain rather than the perception of pain
- Melzack and Wall (1965) were impressed by the ability of emotional and cognitive factors to block pain; they concluded that there must be a circuit descending from the forebrain that can block incoming pain signals **(gate-control theory)**
- the first direct evidence of such a descending analgesia circuit came from the discovery that stimulation of the **periaqueductal gray** (PAG) produced analgesia in rats; surgery could be performed under PAG-stimulation-produced analgesia
- next, it was discovered that there were receptors for opiate analgesics (e.g., morphine) in the PAG and several other sites; this suggested that the body produced its own opiates (called endogenous opiates or **endorphins),** and several were subsequently isolated
- several lines of evidence led Basbaum and Fields to propose a **descending analgesia circuit;** the circuit goes from the PAG to the **raphé nucleus** and then descends via the dorsal columns to the dorsal horns of the spinal cord
- the following are three of the pieces of evidence that support Basbaum and Field's model: (1) microinjection of opiate antagonists, such as naloxone, into the PAG blocks the analgesia produced by

systemic injection of morphine, (2) electrical stimulation of the raphé inhibits pain signals entering the spinal cord, (3) lesioning the raphé or dorsal columns blocks the analgesia produced by PAG stimulation
- one of the most interesting pain phenomena is **phantom limb pain**; it is chronic severe pain that is experienced by about 50% of amputees; paradoxically, surgical treatments have proven ineffective

4.   **Smell and Taste** (see Fig. 7.25 – Fig. 7.27 in *BIOPSYCHOLOGY;* use the **Investigation Olfaction: The Nose Knows** module from the *Beyond the Brain and Behavior CD* for *BIOPSYCHOLOGY;* use *Digital Image Archive Figure CH08F25.BMP* and *CH08F27.BMP)*

a.   **The Olfactory System**

- smell is an olfactory system response to airborne chemicals; there are about **1000 different olfactory receptors,** each having its own special receptor protein
- although there appears to be no organization of receptors at the level of the olfactory mucosa, all receptors having the same receptor protein seem to project to the same area of olfactory bulb **(odotopic mapping)**
- chemical stimuli are processed as follows:

   i)   transduction of olfactory stimuli occurs in olfactory receptors located in the **olfactory mucosa** of the upper nasal cavity;
   ii)   these cells send their axons through the **cribriform plate** to synapse on cells in the **olfactory bulbs**;
   iii)   these neurons then send axons directly to the **piriform cortex** and **amygdala** of the temporal lobes (making olfaction the one sensory modality that gains access to the telencephalon without passing through the thalamus);
   iv)   these areas project to to various parts of the **limbic system** (which is responsible for the emotional perception of odorants) and to the **medial dorsal nucleus of the thalamus**; and
   v)   the dorsomedial nucleus of the thalamus eventually passes the olfactory information on to the **orbitofrontal cortex** where the odor is consciously perceived.

- - **anosmia** is an inability to smell; commonly caused by damage to the olfactory nerves passing through the cribriform plate

b.   **The Gustatory System**

- taste operates in tandem with smell; gustatory receptors are called **taste buds**
- there are 4 primary tastes: **sweet, sour, bitter** and **salty**; however, these perceptions do not match up nicely with 4 simple gustatory receptors…many flavors cannot be recreated by combinations of the primary flavors, there may be a fifth flavor (**umami,** meaning meaty or savoury), and some flavors seem to activate taste neurons by altering neural activity by acting on ion channels directly rather through a receptor
- gustatory stimuli are processed as follows: (1) gustatory stimuli are transduced by taste buds on the tongue and oral cavity; (2) axons from these receptors projects via the **facial nerves** (CN VII), the **glossopharyngeal nerves** (CN IX), and the **vagus nerves** (CN X) to the **solitary nucleus** of the medulla; which projects to (4) the **ventral posterior nucleus** of the thalamus; neurons there relay the gustatory information to (5) **primary gustatory cortex** (near the facial region of SI) and **secondary gustatory cortex** (found deep in the lateral fissure)
- the projections of the gustatory system appear to be largely ipsilateral, unlike the other sensory systems examined
- **ageusia** is an inability to taste; it is rare, but may be caused by damage to the facial nerve
- occasionally anosmia and ageusia occur together, suggesting that at some point olfaction and gustation might be processed in the same area of the brain

5. Selective Attention (see Fig. 7.28 in *BIOPSYCHOLOGY;* use the **Change Blindness** module from the *Beyond the Brain and Behavior CD* for *BIOPSYCHOLOGY)*

- allows us to **consciously perceive** just a fraction of what we **unconsciously sense**
- may be **top-down** or **bottom-up**
- may be focused by internal cognitive processes **(endogenous attention;** believed to be top-down) or by external events **(exogenous attention;** believed to be bottom-up)
- **change blindness** is classic example of the effects of selective attention; it can be demonstrated by **alternately showing** subjects two pictures that are identical in every aspect but one. If there is a **brief delay** between each picture, subjects often take a long time to spot what becomes an obvious difference between the pictures once they are attending to the right location.
- work in both human and nonhuman primates has revealed that different parts of the brain mediate attention to different types of stimuli; for example, faces activate the **ventral visual pathway** while the position of that face activates the **dorsal visual pathway**

Suggested Websites for Lecture 7b:

Supertasters and Taste Intensity: *http://www.sfn.org/content/Publications/BrainBriefings/tastedetectors.html*
From the Society for Neuroscience's *Brain Briefings*, an overview of the tastebuds of the tongue and why some people have better....taste? See also

http://www.sfn.org/content/Publications/BrainBriefings/taste.html

Pain: Controlling Cancer's Pain*: http://www.sciam.com/0996issue/0996foley.html*
From Scientific American, a good article on modern approaches to pain control. See also:

http://www.sciam.com/explorations/0492melzak.html
for an interesting article by Dr. Ronald Melzack on the phenomenon of phantom limbs.

The Somatosensory System: Body: *http://thalamus.wustl.edu/course/body.html*
From the Washington University School of Medicine, a wonderful page devoted to the organization and function of the somatosensory system, including the pain and proprioceptive systems.

The Organs of Smell: *http://www.hhmi.org/senses/d110.html*
Text and figures about the neural bases of smell, from the Howard Hughes Medical Institute. A very good figure of the olfactory pathways in the brain, and information about the vomeronasal organ and the "accessory" olfactory system.

IM-At-A-Glance. Chapter 8: The Sensorimotor System: How You Do What You Do

Detailed Outline	Print Supplements	Media Supplements	Professor's Notes
Chapter 8. The Sensorimotor System: How You Do What You Do pp. 194 - 220 8.1 Three Principles of Sensorimotor Function 8.2 Sensorimotor Association Cortex 8.3 Secondary Motor Cortex 8.4 Primary Motor Cortex 8.5 Cerebellum and Basal Ganglia 8.6 Descending Motor Pathways 8.7 Sensorimotor Spinal Circuits 8.8 Central Sensorimotor Programs	**Instructor's Manual for** *BIOPSYCHOLOGY,* *Lecture 8a and Lecture 8b* **Test Bank for** *BIOPSYCHOLOGY,* *Chapter 8* **Study Guide for** *BIOPSYCHOLOGY,* *Chapter 8* **Transparencies for Physiological Psychology:** *VI. The Sensorimotor System*	***Beyond the Brain & Behavior CD for* BIOPSYCHOLOGY:** *The Beat Goes On Module* *Practice Tests for Chapter 8* *Hard Copy for Chapter 8* *Electronic Flashcards for Chapter 8* **Digital Image Archive, Powerpoint Presentation and Bitmap Images for** *BIOPSYCHOLOGY:* *Chapter 9*	

Lecture 8a

FOREBRAIN STRUCTURES OF THE SENSORIMOTOR SYSTEM

Outline

1. Principles of Sensorimotor Function
    a. Hierarchical Organization
    b. Motor Output is Guided by Sensory Input
    c. Learning Changes the Locus of Sensorimotor Control

2. Posterior Parietal Association Cortex
    a. Apraxia
    b. Contralateral Neglect
    c. Astereognosia

3. Dorsolateral Prefrontal Association Cortex

4. Secondary Motor Cortex

5. Primary Motor Cortex

6. Cerebellum and Basal Ganglia
    a. Cerebellum
    b. Basal Ganglia

Lecture Notes

1. **Principles of Sensorimotor Function** (see Fig. 8.1 in *BIOPSYCHOLOGY;* use *Digital Image Archive Figure CH09F01.BMP)*

    a. **Hierarchical Organization**

        -   the sensorimotor system is organized like a large effective company; the president **(association cortex)** issues general commands and lower levels**(motor neurons and muscles)** take care of details; the advantage of this hierarchical arrangement is that higher levels are left free to focus on complex functions

    b. **Motor Output is Guided by Sensory Input**

        -   like a large company, the sensorimotor system carefully **monitors the external world** and the consequences of its own actions, and it acts accordingly; only **ballistic movements** (brief, all-or-none, high speed movements) are not guided by sensory feedback
        -   note the case of G.O., a former darts champion who suffered an infection that destroyed the somatosensory nerves of his arms; even though he still had visual feedback, he had difficulty picking up buttons or coins, difficulty adjusting to unanticipated external forces, and difficulty maintaining a constant force (e.g., holding a pen, cup, or suitcase)

    c. **Learning Changes the Locus of Sensorimotor Control**

        -   as a new company develops, more and more tasks become part of the routine and are taken over by lower levels of the organization; the same thing happens in the sensorimotor system; after much practice lower levels perform **well-learned tasks** with little higher involvement

    -   why is the sensorimotor system like a large company in these three important respects? Is it mere coincidence? No, they are both complex behavioral systems that have evolved under the pressure to survive in competitive environments; thus it is not surprising that efficient companies and sensorimotor systems have a lot in common

2. **Posterior Parietal Association Cortex** (see Fig. 8.2 and Fig. 8.3 in *BIOPSYCHOLOGY; use Digital Image Archive Figure CH09F02.BMP)*

   - before an effective response can be initiated, the sensorimotor system must know the positions of various parts of the body and of objects in the external world; current thinking is that the **posterior parietal cortex** performs this function
   - the posterior parietal cortex receives input from **visual, auditory,** and **somatosensory systems** (that is why it is considered to be association cortex); most of its output goes to **secondary motor cortices**
   - in addition to disrupting the accuracy of movements, large lesions of posterior cortex can produce **apraxia** and **contralateral neglect**

   a. **Apraxia**

      - apraxia is the inability to perform movements when requested to do so (in the absence of simple sensory or motor deficits, motivational deficits, or intellectual deficits); for example, an apraxic patient may have difficulty demonstrating hammering movements when asked to do so (even when they are demonstrated to him or her) but be perfectly capable of spontaneously hammering a nail
      - apraxia is almost always associated with **left hemisphere** damage, but its symptoms are always bilateral
      - right parietal damage often produces deficits on the **WAIS block-design subtest**; this is referred to as **constructional apraxia**

   b. **Contralateral Neglect**

      - patients with contralateral neglect fail to respond to **visual, auditory,** or **somatosensory** stimuli from the contralateral half of the body
      - contralateral neglect is usually produced by very **large right parietal lesions**
      - patients with contralateral neglect may shave only the right half of their face, eat food from only the right half of their plate, or put only their right leg in their pants; for example, the case of Mrs. S...

3. **Dorsolateral Prefrontal Association Cortex** (see Fig. 8.4 in *BIOPSYCHOLOGY;* use *Digital Image Archive Figure CH09F04.BMP)*

   - projections to this area are from the **posterior parietal cortex**; this area in turn projects to parts of the **secondary motor cortex**, the **primary cortex**, and to the **frontal eye field**
   - research on nonhuman primates has suggested that the prefrontal association cortex is involved in assessments of external stimuli and the initiation of responses to them; neurons here may be activated by the characteristics of an object, its location, or by the response that the object elicits
   - further research shows that the motor neurons firing the earliest (prior to a motor task) are located in the dorsolateral prefrontal cortex, indicating that this area may be key in decisions regarding **voluntary response initiation**

4. **Secondary Motor Cortex** (see Fig. 8.5 in *BIOPSYCHOLOGY;* use *Digital Image Archive Figure CH09F05.BMP)*

   - there are three areas of secondary motor cortex: the **premotor cortex**, the **supplementary motor area**, and the **cingulate motor areas.** They all send information to primary motor cortex; all receive input from primary motor cortex; all are interconnected with one another; and all send axons to the motor circuits of the brainstem
   - functionally, each of these areas produces complex movements when stimulated; are activated both before and during voluntary movements; and are active when either side of the body is involved in a movement

- premotor cortex neurons often respond to both **visual** and **touch stimuli;** it appears to **encode spatial relations** of external cues and **program movements** guided by these cues
- much of the supplementary motor area (SMA) is in the **longitudinal fissure**
- the cingulate motor cortex lies on the cingulate gyrus, just below the SMA
- secondary motor cortex is involved in the planning, programming and generation of complex motor sequences; however, the exact role for each are of secondary motor cortex in this function is not clear

5. **Primary Motor Cortex** (see Fig. 8.6 in *BIOPSYCHOLOGY;* use *Digital Image Archive Figure CH09F07.BMP)*

- **primary motor cortex** is in the **precentral gyrus** of the **frontal lobe;** it is **somatotopically organized;** its organization was discovered by Penfield, who stimulated the cortices of conscious patients during brain surgery
- recent evidence suggests that there is not a 1:1 relationship between a location on the body and its representation on the motor homunculus; instead, the body is **diffusely rep**resented on the homunculus and that these representations can sometimes **overlap**
- the **motor homunculus** has a disproportionate representation of hands and mouth; in fact, two different areas of each primary motor cortex control the contralateral hand
- each area of primary motor cortex receives **feedback** from the muscles and joints that it influences; one of the hand areas receives input from the **skin** rather than the joints and muscles of the digits; this feedback is presumably important for **stereognosis**
- neurons in primary motor cortex seem to code for a **preferred direction of movement;** they fire most just **before and during** the movement; they fire most when the movement is in the **preferred direction** and less as the direction deviates from the preferred one
- lesions of primary motor cortex produce **contralateral astereognosia;** they reduce the **speed** and **force** of contralateral movements, and they make it difficult to move one body part (e.g., a finger) **independently** of others. THEY DO NOT PRODUCE PARALYSIS…

6. **Cerebellum and Basal Ganglia** (use *Digital Image Archive Figure CH03F23.BMP and Figure CH03F31.BMP)*

- the **cerebellum** and **basal ganglia** are both important **subcortical sensorimotor structures,** but neither participates directly in the transmission of signals to the spinal cord
- their role seems to be to **integrate and coordinate** the activity of structures at various levels of the sensorimotor system

a. **Cerebellum**

- the cerebellum (means **little brain**) constitutes only 10% of the brain's mass, but it contains over half the brain's neurons; it is organized systematically in **lobes**
- it receives inputs from **primary** and **secondary motor cortex,** from **brainstem motor nuclei,** and from **somatosensory** and **vestibular** systems
- it is thought to **correct deviations** from intended movements
- effects of diffuse **cerebellar da**mage include loss of the ability to precisely control movement, to adjust motor output to changing conditions, to maintain steady postures, exhibit good locomotion, to maintain balance, to speak clearly, and to control eye movements
- long-recognized role in **motor learning**, and more recently appreciated for a role in the fine-tuning and learning of nonmotor **cognitive responses**

b.   Basal Ganglia (see also Chpt. 3. pp. 73-75)

- the basal ganglia are part of a loop that receives information from various parts of the cortex and transmits it back to **motor cortices** via the **thalamus**
- basal ganglia are involved in **sequencing of movements;** like the cerebellum, its role has recently been expanded to include a variety of **nonmotor cognitive tasks**
- basal ganglia function compromised in patients with **Parkinson's Disease** (due to loss of dopamine from substantia nigra) and **Huntington's Disease** (due to loss of cells in basal ganglia)

Suggested Websites for Lecture 8a:

The Basic Motor Pathway: *http://thalamus.wustl.edu/course/basmot.html*
> From the Washington University School of Medicine, a good text-n-figure description of the corticospinal pathway from motor cortex to the spinal cord.

Basal Ganglia and Cerebellum: *http://thalamus.wustl.edu/course/cerebell.html*
> A very good text-and-figure site from Washington University's School of Medicine, explaining the anatomy and function of the basal ganglia and the cerebellum. Excellent; includes circuit drawings; histological images; well-written.

Gross Anatomy of CNS Motor System: *http://www9.biostr.washington.edu/da.html*
> The Interactive Brain Atlas from the Digital Anatomist Project at the University of Washington; good illustrations of the central motor pathways. From this page, select *Interactive Brain Atlas,* then either 3-D Objects, 3-D Object Composites, or 3-D Pathways for images of the basal ganglia, the cerebellum, and the corticospinal pathways.

Motor Cortex and Movement: *http://www.sciam.com/0696issue/0696techbus02.html*
> An interesting article from Scientific American on what single-unit recordings in primate motor cortex reveal about the neural bases of movement.

Lecture 8b

SPINAL SENSORIMOTOR PATHWAYS AND CIRCUITS

Outline

1. Descending Motor Pathways

2. Sensorimotor Spinal Circuits and Reflexes
   a. Muscles
   b. Muscle Receptor Organs
   c. Withdrawal Reflex
   d. Stretch Reflex
   e. Reciprocal Innervation
   f. Recurrent Collateral Inhibition

3. Central Sensorimotor Programs

Lecture Notes

1. **Descending Motor Pathways** (see Fig. 8.7 and Fig. 8.8 in *BIOPSYCHOLOGY;* use *Digital Image Archive Figure CH09F09.BMP; Figure CH09F10.BMP)*

   - there are four descending motor pathways on each side of the spinal cord; two descend in the dorsolateral areas of the spinal cord: (1) the **dorsolateral corticospinal tract** and (2) the **dorsolateral corticorubrospinal tract;** and two descend in the ventromedial areas of the spinal cord: (3) the **ventromedial corticospinal tract** and (4) the **ventromedial cortico-brainstem-spinal tract**

   1) The Dorsolateral Motor Tracts

   - many axons from primary motor cortex descend through the **medullary** pyramids, decussates, and then continues to descend in the contralateral dorsolateral white matter of the spinal cord. This is the **dorsolateral corticospinal tract.**
   - a second group of axons from primary motor cortex descends to the **red nucleus** of the midbrain. Axons from the red nucleus then decussate and descend through the medulla; some terminate in the nuclei of the cranial nerves, while others continue to descend in the dorsolateral spinal cord. This is the dorsolateral corticorubrospinal tract.
   - most axons in the dorsolateral corticospinal tract and all of those in the dorsolateral corticorubrospinal tract synapse on interneuron pools in the **contralateral spinal gray matter** that control motor neurons of distal limb muscles
   - **Betz cells** in the primary motor cortex descend contralaterally in the dorsolateral corticospinal tract and synapse on **motor neurons** that control the large weight-bearing muscles of the legs
   - primates and a few other mammals capable of **individual digit movement** have dorsolateral corticospinal tract neurons that synapse directly on motor neurons

   2) The Ventromedial Tracts

   - the axons of the ventromedial corticospinal tract **descend ipsilaterally** and **terminate bilaterally** in several segments of the spinal cord on the interneuron pools that control the motor neurons of trunk and proximal limb muscles on both sides of the body; the information delivery is more diffuse and goes to more levels than via dorsolateral paths

- the axons of the ventromedial cortico-brainstem-spinal tract also descend and terminate diffusely in the brainstem on interneurons in the **tectum, vestibular nucleus, reticular formation,** and the nuclei for the **cranial nerves** that innervate the face. From here, axons descend in the ventromedial portion of the spinal cord to influence trunk and proximal limb muscles on both sides of the body
- the different functions of these four tracts are demonstrated by the experiment of Lawrence and Kuypers (1968) on monkeys:

   i) first, they cut the dorsolateral corticospinal tracts at the **medullary pyramids**; the monkeys lost their ability to move individual fingers and to release objects in their grasp (revealing the role of the dorsolateral corticospinal pathway in **individual or fine movements** of the digits); however, they had no difficulty releasing bars and branches when they were climbing

   ii) next all of the monkeys received a second operation:

   a) half of the monkeys received a **dorsolateral corticorubrospinal tract transection;** these monkeys could stand, walk, and climb normally; but when they sat, their arms hung limply by their sides, and they were used like rubber-handled rakes. Thus, the **corticorubrospinal tract** seems to control the **reaching movements of the limbs.**

   b) the other half of the monkeys received a transection of both **ventromedial tracts** (only their dorsolateral corticorubrospinal tract remained intact); these monkeys had great difficulty walking or even sitting (a noise would make them fall over); when they fed, they did so with elbow and whole-hand movements. Thus, the **ventromedial paths** seem to be involved with **whole-body movements** and **postural control.**

2. **Sensorimotor Spinal Circuits and Reflexes** (see Fig. 8.9 - Fig. 8.16 in *BIOPSYCHOLOGY;* use *Digital Image Archive* Digital Image Archive Figure *CH09F14.BMP, Figure CH09F15.BMP, CH09F16.BMP* and *CH09F18.BMP*)

a. **Muscles**

   - review the anatomy of the motor end-plate, the neuromuscular junction, and the role of acetylcholine
   - **motor units** include a single motor neuron and all of the muscle fibers that it innervates; motor unit size is dependent on the movement accuracy required
   - **motor pools** include all motor neurons that innervate fibers of a single muscle
   - **flexors** (bend or flex a joint) vs. **extensors** (straighten or extend a limb)
   - **synergistic** (muscles that produce the same type of movement, either flexion or extension, at a joint) vs. **antagonistic** (muscles whose actions oppose one another at a joint)
   - **dynamic contraction** (one where muscles shorten to produce action at a joint) vs. **isometric contraction** (one where muscle tension increases, but muscle does not shorten and there is not action at joint)

b. **Muscle Receptor Organs**

   - **Golgi tendon organs** are embedded in tendons; **muscle spindles** are embedded in muscles
   - because Golgi tendon organs are connected in **series** with muscles, they are sensitive to muscle tension; in contrast, muscle spindles are connected in **parallel** with the muscle fibers and they are sensitive to muscle length

c. **Stretch Reflex**

   - you have all had your **patellar tendon reflex** tested by a doctor; the doctor raps the tendon of your relaxed thigh muscle, this stretches your thigh muscle and elicits an immediate compensatory contraction that makes your foot swing up; the patellar tendon reflex is a **stretch reflex**
   - notice that this reflex is monosynaptic

- the function of the **intrafusal motor neuron** is to adjust the length of the intrafusal muscle in relation to extrafusal muscle length to maintain the muscle spindle's sensitivity to changes in extrafusal muscle length
- the function of the muscle-spindle feedback circuit is to make automatic adjustments in muscle tension in response to external forces
- the brain sends general instructions to the motor neurons (e.g., hold the glass of water), and the muscle spindle feedback circuit automatically adjusts the activity in the motor neurons to make sure that this instruction is carried out even if there are unanticipated external influences (e.g., somebody brushing against the arm)

d. Withdrawal Reflex

- sensory neurons carrying signals evoked by a painful stimulus to a hand or foot synapse on interneurons that synapse on flexors of the same limb
- thus, about 1.6 millisecond (the time for a signal to be transmitted across a two synapses) after the painful stimulus, a burst of action potentials can be recorded in the flexor motor nerves of the same limb, and the limb is withdrawn
- the limb is withdrawn before information about the painful event reaches the brain

e. Reciprocal Innervation

- when a muscle contracts, **antagonist muscles** automatically relax; this is mediated by inhibitory interneurons
- however, there is always some degree of **co-contraction**, for smoother, more precise movement

f. Recurrent Collateral Inhibition

- when a motor neuron fires, an ax**on collateral** feeds onto an **inhibitory interneuron** in the ventral horn (i.e., onto a **Renshaw cell**), which synapses on the cell body of the motor neuron that activated it; thus motor neurons take an enforced rest after firing; this **distributes the work load** among the muscle's motor pool)

4. Central Sensorimotor Programs (see Fig. 8.17 and Fig. 8.18 in *BIOPSYCHOLOGY;* use *The Beat Goes On* module for the **Beyond the Brain & Behavior CD for *BIOPSYCHOLOGY*)**

- the **central sensorimotor program** theory suggests that all but the highest levels of the senorimotor system have certain activities programmed into them; complex movements are produced by activating the appropriate combinations of these programs which are then executed without the need for control from higher levels in the system
- central sensorimotor programs are capable of **motor equivalence;** the same task can be solved in different ways. Control of this equivalence appears to be high in the system; for example, you can sign you name using your hand or your foot...in either case, the signatures are very similar AND the secondary motor cortex for the preferred hand is activated (even when the foot signs)
- Grillner (1985) showed that coordinated walking movements occurred in cats whose brains had been separated from their spinal cord if the cats were held over a treadmill; this suggests that the programs for some complex motor activities are wired into the spinal cord; these **central sensorimotor programs** are analogous to the protocols for a procedural automation
- the sensory information that controls central sensorimotor programs do not have to be consciously perceived
- many complex **species-typical behaviors** do not have to be practiced for the central sensorimotor programs to develop; however, for many other behaviors practice is essential. This sensorimotor learning **"chunks"** central sensorimotor programs and **transfers control** to lower levels of the CNS.

- functional brain imaging (PET) during sensorimotor learning has revealed that:

i) although **posterior parietal cortex** is active during performance of both new and well-practiced motor sequences, it is most active during new sequences. This is because posterior parietal cortex integrates sensory stimuli that guide motor sequences, and it is most active when stimuli are actively attended to (as would happen during learning of new motor sequences).

ii) **dorsolateral prefrontal cortex** is active during performance of new motor sequences but not well-practiced motor sequences; thus, this brain area may be most involved when motor sequences are largely under conscious control

iii) **premotor cortex** is most active (contralaterally) when a motor sequence is new; **supplementary motor cortex** is most active (bilaterally) during well-practiced motor sequences. Thus, premotor cortex is more important when a behavior is guided by sensory stimuli whereas the supplementary motor cortex may be more important when a behavior can be performed automatically, with little sensory feedback necessary.

iv) contralateral **motor cortex** and **somatosensory cortex** were active during both new and well-practiced motor sequences.

v) contralateral **basal ganglia** were active during both new and well-practiced motor sequences.

vi) **cerebellum** was active bilaterally were active during both new and well-practiced motor sequences, but was most active during new sequences.

Suggested Websites for Lecture 8b:

Spinal Mechanisms of Movement: *http://thalamus.wustl.edu/course/spinal.html*
See this site for a good description of the organization of motor pathways in the spinal cord, and of the spinal circuits involved in the deep-tendon (muscle stretch) reflex and the golgi tendon organ (GTO) reflex. See also:

http://www.ptd.neu.edu/neuroanatomy/cyberclass/spinalcontrol/

for another excellent source of information about spinal mechanisms of movement.

Myasthenia Gravis and Disorders of the Neuromuscular Junction:
http://www.neuro.wustl.edu/neuromuscular/index.html

From Washington University's School of Medicine, a great resource on neuromuscular disorders.

Animation of the Stretch Reflex:
http://psychlab1.hanover.edu/Classes/Neuro/Internet/Stretch%20Reflex/index.html

From John Krantz at Hanover College, an animation of the stretch reflex; requires the Powerpoint Animation viewer (which can be downloaded from this site).

**IM-AT-A-GLANCE: Chapter 9. Development of the Nervous System:
From Fertilized Egg to You**

Detailed Outline	Print Supplements	Media Supplements	Professor's Notes
Chapter 9. Development of the Nervous System: From Fertilized Egg to You pp. 221 - 239 9.1 Phases of Neurodevelopment 9.2 Postnatal Cerebral Development in Human Infants 9.3 Effects of Experience on Neurodevelopment 9.4 Neuroplasticity in Adults 9.5 Disorders of Neurodevelopment: Autism and Williams Syndrome	**Instructor's Manual for** *BIOPSYCHOLOGY,* *Lecture 9a and Lecture 9b* **Test Bank for** *BIOPSYCHOLOGY,* *Chapter 9* **Study Guide for** *BIOPSYCHOLOGY,* *Chapter 9* **Transparencies for Physiological Psychology:** *II. The Anatomy of the Nervous System: Plate TR15. Development of the Nervous System*	*Beyond the Brain & Behavior CD for* **BIOPSYCHOLOGY:** *Practice Tests for Chapter 9* *Hard Copy for Chapter 9* *Electronic Flashcards for Chapter 9* **Digital Image Archive, Powerpoint Presentation and Bitmap Images for** *BIOPSYCHOLOGY:* *Chapter 15* **Biological Psychology Video, Segment 13.** *Development of the Brain*	

Lecture 9a
NEURAL DEVELOPMENT

Outline

1. Induction of the Neural Plate

2. Neural Proliferation

3. Migration and Aggregation

4. Axon Growth and the Formation of Synapses
   a. Chemoaffinity Hypothesis
   b. Blueprint Hypothesis
   c. Topographic-Gradient Hypothesis

5. Neural Death and Synapse Rearrangement

Lecture Notes

- each product of sexual reproduction begins life as a single cell (**zygote**)
- during the development of the **embryo**, the first observable step in the development of the nervous system is the induction of the **neural plate**

1. **Induction of the Neural Plate** (see Fig. 9.1 in *BIOPSYCHOLOGY;* use *Digital Image Archive Figure CH15F01.BMP*)

   - about 3 weeks after conception, a patch of **ectoderm** on the dorsal surface of the embryo becomes distinguishable from the rest of the ectoderm; this patch is the **neural plate,** and it eventually develops into the nervous system
   - prior to induction of the neural plate, the cells of the dorsal ectoderm are **totipotential** (that is, if they are transplanted to a new site in the embryo, they develop in the same way as cells at the new site); these cells are called **stem cells**
   - after neural plate induction, the cells there lose some of their totipotentiality; they can develop into any kind of neuron, but not any other kind of cell. These cells are said to be **pluripotent.**
   - the development of the neural plate seems to be **induced** by the underlying **mesoderm**; in one experiment, a piece of mouse mouth mesoderm was implanted next to the ectoderm of a chick embryo, and recognizable teeth were induced to develop from the chick ectoderm
   - the neural plate develops into the **neural groove** and then into the **neural tube**, which subsequently develops into the CNS. By 40 days, the anterior end of the neural tube develops 3 swellings that become the **forebrain, midbrain** and **hindbrain.**

2. **Neural Proliferation**

   - after the neural tube is formed, the developing nervous system cells rapidly increase in number
   - cell division occurs in the **ventricular zone** of the neural tube (the zone next to the ventricle); when they leave the cell division cycle, cells migrate into other layers

3. **Migration and Aggregation** (see Fig. 9.2 and Fig. 9.3 in *BIOPSYCHOLOGY;* use *Digital Image Archive Figure CH15F03.BMP)*

    - cells migrate away from the ventricular zone along a temporary network of **radial glial cells**, which are present in only the developing neural tube
    - the cells of the neocortex migrate in an **inside-out pattern**; the deepest layers form first so that the cells of the superficial layers must migrate through them
    - migration of the cells of the **neural crest** is of particular interest because these cells ultimately form the PNS, and thus many have a long way to migrate
    - neural crest cells transplanted to a new part of the neural crest migrate to the destination that is appropriate for cells in the new location; thus the migration routes must be encoded in the medium through which they travel rather than in the cells themselves; many different types of chemicals signals have been found that guide the migration of the axons of future PNS neurons
    - once migration is complete, cells must **aggregate** correctly to form various neural structures; this is hypothesized to be mediated by specialized neural cell **adhesion molecules** in the cell membranes (NCAMs)

4. **Axon Growth and the Formation of Synapses** (see Fig. 9.4 – Fig. 9.7 in *BIOPSYCHOLOGY;* use *Digital Image Archive Figure CH15F05.BMP; CH15F06.BMP; CH15F07.BMP;* and *CH15F08.BMP)*

    - once the aggregation of developing neurons is complete, axons and dendrites grow out from the neurons; growing to the correct target is particularly difficult for axons that have a long way to grow
    - studies in which the same recognizable developing neuron has been labeled in different subjects demonstrate that the axons of some particular neurons grow to the same destination by the same route in every member of a species; this accurate axon growth seems to be directed by a **growth cone** at the growing axon tip
    - three hypotheses have been proposed to explain how growth cones make their way to their correct destination: (1) the **chemoaffinity hypothesis**, (2) the **blueprint hypothesis**, and (3) the **topographic-gradient hypothesis**
    - axon growth is often studied in **regenerating** neurons; it is assumed that axonal growth and regrowth are guided by the same mechanisms

    a. **Chemoaffinity Hypothesis**

    - Sperry's classic eye-rotation regeneration experiments remain the classic example of data supporting the **chemoaffinity hypothesis**
    - Sperry cut the optic nerves of frogs, **rotated** their eyes, and waited for regeneration; after regeneration, it was clear from their **misdirected feeding** responses that the visual world of the frogs was rotated by the same degree as the eye rotation, the axons seemed to have regenerated back to their **original targets**
    - on the basis of this series of studies, Sperry proposed the chemoaffinity hypothesis; the hypothesis that the target of each growing axon has a **specific chemical** that draws the correct growing axon to it
    - but the chemoaffinity hypothesis can't explain why some neurons grow to their correct targets via indirect routes or why a target structure transplanted to an unnatural site becomes incorrectly innervated
    - in addition, there are not enough genes in each cell for each neuron to produce and release its own distinct chemical label

    b. **Blueprint hypothesis**

    - another problem with the chemoaffinity hypothesis is that it cannot explain how some developing axons follow the **same indirect route** in every member of a species
    - the **blueprint hypothesis** (the hypothesis that the substrate contains physical and chemical trails that growth cones follow to their correct destinations) was proposed to account for the accuracy of axon growth
    - only the first axon that grows into an area must have the ability to reach its correct target; it is guided by **CAMs** of cells along the route

- the others appear to follow the **pioneer growth cone's** route by a process called **fasciculation**; if a pioneer axon growth cone is destroyed by a laser, few of the other neurons in the nerve reach their correct destinations.
- but the blueprint hypothesis cannot explain how some developing axons manage to grow to their correct targets even when their starting points have been surgically shifted. For example, Lance-Jones and Landmesser (1980) cut out a piece of the spinal cord of a chick embryo, inverted it, and reimplanted it; nevertheless, the axons grew out to their correct targets

    c.   **Topographic-Gradient Hypothesis**

- the **topographic-gradient hypothesis** is that axon growth from one topographic array (such as a **retina)** to another (the **optic tectum)** is guided by the relative position of the cell bodies and terminals on two **intersecting gradients** (up-down and left-right) of chemicals on the originating tissue (the retina, in this case)
- the topographic-gradient hypothesis is supported by the fact that lesions of part of optic tectum cause optic nerve axons that have been transected to grow out to fill the available space in relation to their position on a two-dimensional topographic map of the retina, regardless of how much tectum is left. Similarly, lesions of the part of the retina cause regenerating axons to fill the optic tectum in a way that matches the topography of the remaining retina

    Summary: all the evidence on axon growth and regeneration suggests that a variety of mechanisms can guide axon growth; the growth of different axons appears to be guided by different combinations of these mechanisms

5.   **Neuron Death and Synapse Rearrangement** (see Fig. 9.8 in *BIOPSYCHOLOGY;* use *Digital Image Archive Figure CH15F08.BMP)*

- up to 50% of neurons that develop die during the course of normal development; the fact that neurons that make incorrect connections are more likely to die suggests that cell death increases the overall accuracy of synaptic connections
- three lines of evidence suggest that neurons die because they fail to compete successfully for some life-preserving factor (**neurotrophins** such as **nerve growth factor**) supplied by their target:

    i) implantation of an **extra target site** decreases neuron death (e.g., an implanted extra limb decreases motor neuron loss);
    ii) destroying some neurons before the period of neuron death **increases the survival rate** of the remainder; and
    iii) increasing the number of axons that initially synapse on a target **decreases survival rate** of the remainder

- most of this cell death is due to **apoptosis;** preprogrammed cell death that is believed to result from the lack of an appropriate trophic factor.
- in addition, there is **synapse rearrangement** during an organism's lifespan; its effect is to focus the output of each neuron on fewer postsynaptic neurons

Suggest Websites for Lecture 9a:

Brain Development: *http://faculty.washington.edu/chudler/dev.html*
    From Dr. Eric Chudler at the University of Washington; good text and figures, and many good links to other relevant websites.

Growth Cones: *http://www.ucsf.edu/neurosc/faculty/Sretavan/Eph-timelapse.html*
    B&W movies of the growth cones of retinal ganglion cells, from Dr. David Sretevan at UCSF.

Degeneration, Regeneration, and Reorganization: *http://www.hhmi.org/senses/e/e210.htm*
    From the Howard Hughes Medical Center, an article describing the reorganization of a person's somatosensory homunculus after surgery. Brief but interesting.

Lecture 9b
POSTNATAL NEURAL DEVELOPMENT AND
NEURODEVELOPMENTAL DISORDERS

Outline

1. Postnatal Cerebral Development in Humans
   a. Postnatal Growth of the Human Brain
   b. Development of Prefrontal Cortex

2. Effects of Experience on Neurodevelopment

3. Neuroplasticity in Adults

4. Disorders of Neurodevelopment
   a. Autism
   b. Williams Syndrome

Lecture Notes

1. Postnatal Cerebral Development in Humans

- the human brain develops more slowly than other species, not maturing until late adolescence.
- in particular, the **prefrontal cortex** is the last part of the brain to reach maturity, and it is thought to mediate many **higher cognitive abilities.**

a. Postnatal Growth of the Human Brain

- brain volume quadruples between birth and adulthood; most of this increase in volume comes from increased numbers of synapses **(synaptogenesis)**; **myelination** of axons; and increased **dendritic branching**
- synaptogenesis is assumed to indicated increased analytic ability in a brain region; synaptogenesis in the the visual cortex peaks at about 4 months postnatal, whereas in prefrontal cortex maximal density is reached in the second year
- myelination increases the speed of axonal conduction; again, sensory and motor areas are myelinated in the first few months of life while the prefrontal cortex is not fully myelinated until adolescence
- many synapses that form early in development are eventually lost; overproduction of synapses in the young brain may contribute to its greater **plasticity**

b. Development of Prefrontal Cortex

- parallels the course of **human cognitive development**
- linked to 3 main types of cognitive function: **working memory,** or the ability to keep information accessible for short periods of time; **planning & completing** sequences of actions; and **inhibiting inappropriate responses.**
- Diamond (1991) found that damage to prefrontal cortex leads to **perseverative errors** in adults, so that their behavior looks more like an infants.

2. Effects of Experience on Neurodevelopment (see Fig. 9.9 in **BIOPSYCHOLOGY**)

- neurodevelopment results from an **interaction** between neurons and their environment
- **KEY RULE:** neurons and synapses that are not activated by experience do not usually survive.
- researchers have found that depriving one eye of input for just a few days early in life blocks the development of vision in that eye and the normal development of **ocular dominance columns;** this is due in part to a **decrease in axonal sprouting** of thalamic neurons terminating in visual cortex
- in a graphic example of the competition that underlies synapse rearrangement, Lo and Poo (1991) demonstrated *in vitro* that stimulating one of two motor neurons that innervated the same muscle cell caused a **rapid degradation** of synaptic contacts between the other, inactive motor neuron and the muscle cell
- there is some evidence that early musical training influences the organization of human auditory cortex; using fMRI, researchers have found that such training expands the part of auditory cortex that responds to complex musical tones
- experience alters neural development in at least 3 different ways: 1) by influencing gene expression for **cell adhesion molecules**; 2) by influencing the release of **neurotrophins**; and 3) by altering the **spontaneous activity** of certain brain regions
- simply placing an adult animal in an **enriched environment** can increase neurogenesis in brain regions such as the hippocampus

3. Plasticity in Adults

- it has only recently been appreciated that the adult brain is capable of considerable plasticity
- this is due in part to evidence that **neurogenesis** occurs in the adult brain; for example, Nottebohm and his colleagues demonstrated an annual increase in neurons in song-production centers in the brains of adult male birds
- neurogenesis has since been demonstrated in the **hippocampus,** the **olfactory bulbs,** and **association cortex**
- there is also evidence for **functional reorganization** of cortex in adult vertebrates, including humans
- for example, repeated active identification of somatosensory stimuli can expand the representation of the areas that are stimulated in the **somatosensory homunculus**

4. Disorders of Neurodevelopment (see Fig. 9.10 and Fig. 9.11 in **BIOPSYCHOLOGY**)

- during the course of development, even a small perturbation in the normal course of events can have dire consequences

a. Autism

- occurs in 0.0004% of the population
- emerges by the age of 3; individuals cannot interpret the **emotions** or intentions of others; cannot interact **socially;** and tend to be **preoccupied** by a single event or subject

- although autism is a **heterogeneous disorder,** most patients have some preserved abilities (e.g., musical)
- **autistic savants** are autistic patients who display amazing and specific cognitive abilities such as feats of memory, drawing, or playing musical instruments
- **genetic factors** play a role in autism; there is a 5% chance of autism in the siblings of an autistic person, and a 60% chance if that sibling is a monozygotic twin
- neurodevelopment in the **first month of pregnancy** seems to be a key, based on the fact that **thalidomide** has been linked to the development of an autistic condition and that defects in the development of the ears is often observed; thalidomide was generally taken, and the ears develop, within the first weeks of conception
- there is often a defect in the development of the parts of the **brainstem** that control the muscles of the face in people with autism; this is often accompanied by defects in **cerebellar development**

b. Williams Syndrome

- even more rare than autism; occurs in about 0.0005% of all births
- have **language skills** that far exceed their generally low IQs; speech is often **animated** and very **descriptive**
- patients with Williams Syndrome have very **impaired spatial abilities** and **underdeveloped parietal** and **occipital cortices**; this appears to be due to a major mutation in **chromosome 7**

Suggest Websites for Lecture 9b:

Autism Society of America: *http://www.autism-society.org/*
A good resource for information about this neurodevelopmental disorder; April is National Autism Awareness Month

Williams Syndrome Association: *http://www.williams-syndrome.org/*
More information about this neurodevelopmental disorder.

Experience and Ocular Dominance Columns: *http://www.hhmi.org/senses/b220.html*
Information from the Howard Hughes Medical Institute; from this page, select the Sidebar *"Urgent Need to Use Two Eyes"*.

IM-AT-A-GLANCE: Chapter 10. Brain Damage and Neuroplasticity:
Can the Brain Recover from Damage?

Detailed Outline	Print Supplements	Media Supplements	Professor's Notes
Chapter 10. Brain Damage and Neuroplasticity: Can the Brain Recover from Damage? pp. 240-267 10.1 Causes of Brain Damage 10.2 Neuropsychological Diseases 10.3 Animal Models of Human Neuropsychological Diseases 10.4 Neuroplastic Responses to Nervous System Damage: Degeneration, Regeneration, Reorganization & Recovery 10.5 Neuroplasticity and the Treatment of Nervous System Damage	**Instructor's Manual for** ***BIOPSYCHOLOGY,*** *Lecture 10a, Lecture 10, & Lecture 10c* **Test Bank for** ***BIOPSYCHOLOGY,*** *Chapter 10* **Study Guide for** ***BIOPSYCHOLOGY,*** *Chapter 10* **Transparencies for Physiological Psychology:** *XI. Learning, Memory and Neural Plasticity*	***Beyond the Brain & Behavior CD for*** **BIOPSYCHOLOGY:** *My Tumor and Welcome To It Module* *Practice Tests for Chapter 10* *Hard Copy for Chapter 10* *Electronic Flashcards for Chapter 10* **Digital Image Archive, Powerpoint Presentation and Bitmap Images for** ***BIOPSYCHOLOGY:*** *Chapter 6 Chapter 15* **Biological Psychology Video, Segment 6.** *Pathology Examples of Healthy and Damaged Human Brains*	

Lecture 10a
BRAIN DAMAGE AND
HUMAN NEUROPSYCHOLOGICAL DISEASES

Outline

1. Causes of Brain Damage

    a. Tumors
    b. Cerebrovascular Disorders
    c. Closed-Head Injuries
    d. Infections
    e. Neurotoxins
    f. Genetic Factors

2. Neuropsychological Diseases
    a. Epilepsy
    b. Parkinson's Disease
    c. Huntington's Disease
    d. Multiple Sclerosis
    e. Alzheimer's Disease

Lecture Notes

1. **Causes of Brain Damage:** (see Fig. 10.1 – 10.7 in *BIOPSYCHOLOGY;* use *Digital Image Archive Figure CH6F04.BMP;* use *Beyond the Brain & Behavior CD, My Tumor and Welcome to It* module; use *Biological Psychology Video, Segment 6. Pathology Examples of Healthy and Damaged Brains*)

- much can be learned about the brain's normal functioning by examining deficits after brain damage

   a. Tumors
   - a tumor **(neoplasm)** is a group of cells growing independently of the rest of the body; a tumor can be **encapsulated** or **infiltrating**; it can be **benign** or **malignant**
   - **metastatic tumors** are tumors that originate in one organ and spread to another; the symptoms of multiple cerebral tumors are often the first signs of lung cancer
   - 20% of brain tumors are **meningiomas** that grow in the meninges; they are encapsulated and benign

   b. Cerebrovascular Disorders
   - **"stroke"** is commonly used to refer to any cerebrovascular disorder of sudden onset
   - may be due to **cerebral hemorrhage;** the bursting of **aneurysms** (balloon-like dilations of weak areas of blood vessels) is a major cause of intracerebral bleeding; aneurysms can be **congenital** or the result of infection, toxins etc.
   - **cerebral ischemia** is a disruption of blood supply to an area of the brain;

        (1) in **thrombosis** a plug (a **thrombus**) becomes lodged at its site of formation; the plug may be due to a blood clot, fat, oil, cancerous cells, air bubbles, etc.;
        (2) in **embolism** a plug (an **embolus**) travels from its site of formation and becomes lodged in a smaller blood vessel; and
        (3) in **arteriosclerosis** the blood vessel walls thicken and the space inside narrows; usually from the accumulation of fat

- the brain damage caused during an ischemic episode is believed to be due to an excessive release of **excitatory amino acids**
- **glutamate,** the brain's most prevalent excitatory amino acid neurotransmitter, is released in excessive quantities when blood vessels are blocked
- the excessive glutamate overactivates glutamate receptors on postsynaptic membrane sites thus too many Na+ and Ca++ ions are allowed to enter the postsynaptic neuron; the over abundance of Na+ and Ca++ triggers either (a) an excessive release of glutamate, causing a cascade of this toxic effect or, (b) triggers a sequence of reactions that kills the postsynaptic neuron
- the brain damage caused by ischemia takes a while to develop; does not occur equally in all regions of the brain; and the exact physiological mechanism for such damage varies from region to region
- researchers are currently studying the ability of **NMDA receptor blockers** administered directly after a stroke to reduce subsequent brain damage

c. **Closed-head Injuries**
  - a brain **contusion** is an injury in which there is bleeding from the brain in the absence of a **laceration;** the bleeding results in a **hematoma** (a bruise or collection of clotted blood); contusions are caused by the brain hitting the skull, and they are often *contre coup* (on other side of brain from blow)
  - **concussion** is the diagnosis when a blow to the head disrupts consciousness, but no evidence of physical damage can be found; the **punch-drunk syndrome** is general dementia due to an accumulation of many concussions

d. **Infections**
  - **encephalitis** is the general term for inflammation of the brain resulting from infection
  - **bacterial infections** can be treated with antibiotics, but if left untreated they can cause **meningitis** (inflammation of meninges), **brain abscesses** (pockets of pus), and **general paresis** (a syndrome of insanity and dementia)
  - **viral infections** include infections that preferentially attack the nervous system (e.g., **rabies virus**) and infections that show no preference for the nervous system but they sometimes attack it (e.g., **mumps and herpes viruses**)
  - viruses may play a key role in the etiology of many neuropsychological disorders; their role is often hard to study because they may lie **dormant** not produce symptoms until years after they invade the nervous system

e. **Neurotoxins**
  - brain damage can be produced by a variety of toxins in the environment; "mad hatters" were the result of **mercury poisoning**; "crackpots" were originally those who drank tea from cracked ceramic pots with **lead** cores; the result was poisoning
  - sometimes drugs used to treat a disease can have neurotoxic effects; for example, **tardive dyskinesia** is a disorder produced by prolonged exposure to certain antipsychotic medications

f. **Genetic Factors**
  - some genetic disorders are accidents of cell division; e.g., in **Down syndrome** an extra chromosome in pair 21 is present in all cells; this extra chromosome produces characteristic **physical alterations** and **retarded intellectual development**
  - more commonly, genetic disorders are products of abnormal genes; these genes are usually **recessive,** as **dominant genes** that disturb neuropsychological function tend to be eliminated from the gene pool

g. **Programmed Cell Death**
  - **dysfunctional neurons** and other cells are often eliminated by activating genes that kill them; this programmed cell death is called **apoptosis.**
  - this is more adaptive than **necrosis,** in which neurons die passively as a result of injury. Apoptosis begins at the **nucleus** of the neuron and takes days; necrosis does not alter the nucleus until late in the process, which generally takes only a few hours.

2. Neuropsychological Disorders (see Fig. 10.8 – 10.13 in *BIOPSYCHOLOGY;* use *Digital Image Archive Figure CH6F07.BMP, CH6F09.BMP* and *CH06F12.BMP)*

a. Epilepsy

- epilepsy is any disorder in which epileptic seizures recur **spontaneously**
- when **convulsions** (motor seizures) are present, epilepsy is easy to diagnose; convulsions often involve **clonus** (tremor), **tonus** (rigidity), loss of balance, and/or loss of consciousness
- however, many seizures involve subtle changes in thought, mood, and/or behavior with no convulsive symptoms whatsoever
- the observation of **epileptic spikes** in the EEG is incontrovertible evidence of epilepsy; however, failure to observe them does not prove that the person is not epileptic
- epileptic **auras** sometimes precede an epileptic seizure
- there are two main classes of seizures: **partial seizures** and **generalized seizures**

i) Partial Seizures

- partial seizures are those that do not involve the entire brain
- **simple partial seizures** are partial seizures whose symptoms are primarily sensory and/or motor; usually the symptoms start in one part of the body and spread to other parts of the body as discharges spread through the sensory and motor areas of the brain
- **complex partial seizures** are often restricted to the **temporal lobes;** the motor symptoms of complex partial seizures vary in complexity from **automatisms** (simple, compulsive, repeated behaviors such as tugging on a piece of hair) to long sequences of behavior that are out of context and slightly peculiar but are, for the most part, normal-appearing
- epileptics typically have **no memory** for the events of a complex partial seizure

ii) Generalized Seizures

- generalized seizures are involve the entire brain; they may start from a **focus** and gradually spread, or they may begin almost simultaneously throughout the entire brain;
- include **grand mal seizures** ("big trouble") (**tonic-clonic**, loss of balance and consciousness, tongue biting, **incontinence**, turning blue from **hypoxia**) and **petit mal seizures** ("little trouble") (petit mal absence, 3-per-second spike-and-wave

b. Parkinson's Disease

- Parkinson's disease attacks 0.5% of the population; it usually develops in people in their 50s or 60s, and is more common in **males**
- the first symptom is often a **tremor** or **stiffness of the fingers** (the same symptoms seen in many other long- and short-term disorders)
- symptoms of the full-blown disorder are **tremor at rest, muscular rigidity, slowness of movement**, and a **masklike face**
- there is no intellectual deterioration (no **dementia**)
- its cause is unknown, but it is associated with degeneration of **dopamine** neurons in the **substantia nigra**; these neurons project to the **striatum**
- treated with **L-DOPA**, the metabolic precursor of dopamine

c. Huntington's Disease

- like Parkinson's disease, it is a **motor disorder;** unlike Parkinson's disease, it is inherited but rare, its cause is understood, and it is always associated with **dementia**
- its main symptoms are **complex jerky movements** of entire limbs; dementia occurs later in the disease, which is always fatal
- Huntington's disease is caused by a single **dominant gene**; 50% of all offspring of a Huntington's parent will get it; the reason the disease has not disappeared is that the first symptoms do not appear until after the age of reproduction (at 40-50 years of age)

- the abnormal gene responsible for Huntington's disease produces an abnormal protein called **huntingtin;** its function in the brain is unknown

d. Multiple Sclerosis

- MS is a disease of CNS **myelin;** degeneration of the myelin sheaths eventually leads to a breakdown of myelin and the associated axons and the development of areas of hard scar tissue throughout the CNS; "sclerosis" means "hardening"
- the symptoms depend on the location of the scars; but common symptoms are **ataxia** (loss of motor coordination), weakness, numbness, tremor, and poor vision
- there are often periods of partial recovery from the disease, but there are no exceptions to the generally worsening progression of the disorder
- it is more common in cool climates; it is rare among gypsies and Asians; there is a genetic component, as the concordance rate is 36% in **monozygotic** twins and 12% in **dizygotic** twins
- **experimental allergic encephalomyelitis** is an animals model of MS; it can be produced in animals by injecting them with myelin and a substance that stimulates the body's immune reaction; this has led to the hypothesis that that MS results from a faulty immune reaction against the body's own myelin, perhaps resulting from an early infection or toxin

e. Alzheimer's Disease

- 15% of people over 65 and 35% over 85 years old suffer from Alzheimer's disease
- the first signsare a decline in cognitive ability (e.g. forgetfulness) and emotional instability (e.g. depression); eventually there is total **dementia** and an inability to perform even the most simple responses (e.g., swallowing); it is **terminal**
- can only by definitively diagnosed by autopsy and the discovery of **amyloid plaques** (clumps of degenerating neurons and an abnormal protein called **amyloid**), and tangles of **neurofibrils** within neurons
- loss of neurons is common; plaques, tangles and neuron loss are often most common in areas involved in memory such as the **hippocampus, amygdala,** and **entorhinal cortex**
- appears to be a clear genetic component; people with an immediate family member suffering from Alzheimer's disease have a 50% chance of developing the disease if they live into their 80's
- **cholinergic** neurons often die early in the course of Alzheimer's disease; **cholinergic** agonists are effective at reducing symptoms early in the disease

Suggested Websites for Lecture 10a:

Brain Trauma: *http://www.med.harvard.edu/AANLIB/*
> The Whole Brain Atlas excellent images and time-lapse movies of various brain trauma, including stroke, Alzheimer's disease, Huntington's disease, and MS.

Huntington's Disease: *http://www.hdsa.org/*
> From the Huntington's Disease Society of America, a good resource for those interested in the etiolgy and cause of HD.

Parkinson's Disease:

> *http://medweb.bham.ac.uk/http/depts/clin_neuro/teaching/tutorials/parkinsons/parkinsons1.html*

> An abysmally long URL, but a great site from the Department of Clinical Neurosciences at the University of Birmingham, England; note the references to James Parkinson's original monograph, the links to the anatomical correlates of Parkinson's Disease, and the QuickTime movies of patients displaying the symptoms of Parkinson's Disease.

The Parkinson's Institute: http://www.parkinsonsinstitute.org/index.html
> Founded by Dr. William Langston, of MPTP fame...a good source of basic information about a variety of movement disorders (including Parkinson's disease).

Lecture 10b
ANIMAL MODELS OF
HUMAN NEUROPSYCHOLOGICAL DISORDERS

Outline

1. Kindling Model of Epilepsy

3. Transgenic Mouse Model of Alzheimer's Disease

4. MPTP Model of Parkinson's Disease

Lecture Notes

1. Kindling Model of Epilepsy

-   the typical kindling experiment begins with an animal (usually a rat) receiving a mild, brief electrical **brain stimulation** (usually to the **amygdala**) about once per day
-   the first stimulation has no behavioral effect; however, after a few days of stimulations a mild convulsion involving **clonic jaw movements** is elicited; with further stimulation the convulsions elicited by each stimulation become longer and longer and more and more generalized, and eventually produces a **fully generalized convulsion**
-   kindling can be produced by the periodic stimulation of many brain sites other than the amygdala; it can be produced by the periodic administration of initially subconvulsive doses of **convulsive drugs;** and it can be elicited in many different species
-   kindling does not occur at all at short interstimulation intervals (less than 20 minutes or so); and it takes many more stimulations to kindle if the intervals are less than an hour or so
-   the most interesting and important aspect of kindling is its **permanence**
-   the kindling paradigm has been used as to study epilepsy in two ways:

    i)   the convulsions elicited in kindled animals have been used as an **animal model** of different types of human epilepsy; and
    ii)   the physiological changes that underlie kindling has been used as an animal model of the development of epilepsy (**epileptogenesis**) sometimes observed after a **head injury**

-   kindled convulsions are usually not **spontaneous;** however, if animals are kindled long enough (e.g., 300 stimulations in rats), they will eventually become truly epileptic; they will have convulsions that recur spontaneously even after the stimulations have been curtailed.
-   the **interictal behavioral changes** seen in these animals often mimic changes observed in human epileptics

2. Transgenic Mouse Model of Alzheimer's Disease

-   the most exciting advance in **Alzheimer's disease research** in many years; area has needed a good animal model of the disease
-   problem is that only humans and a few nonhuman primates develop **amyloid plaques,** a hallmark of the disease; this has prevented researchers from studying the role of plaques in the neurodegeneration that is observed in Alzheimer's disease (are plaques a cause or a consequence of the degeneration?)
-   in one example of the transgenic mouse model of Alzheimer's disease, genes that accelerate human amyloid development are injected into fertilized mouse embryos
-   as mice mature, their brains develop amyloid plaques with a distribution similar to that seen in human patients (e.g., highest in hippocampus and surrounding areas)
-   unfortunately, these mice do not develop **neurofibrillary tangles;** in addition, the degree of **memory impairment** does not change as the mice mature and develop more plaques

3. MPTP Model of Parkinson's Disease

- this particular animal model grew out of a tragic human accident
- in 1982, several **young people** were admitted to hospital with **severe Parkinson's symptoms;** this was surprising because such severe cases are not usually seen before the age of 50
- it was discovered that all were **opiate addicts** who had recently used an **synthetic opiate** made by the same person; some of the batch was obtained, and it was found to contain a neurotoxin called **MPTP**
- the similarity between the MPTP syndrome and Parkinson's disease was remarkable; even minor symptoms of Parkinson's disease such as **seborrhea** (oily skin) and **micrographia** (very small handwriting) were present
- this suggested that Parkinson's disease might be effectively studied in an **MPTP animal model;** it was quickly established that **laboratory primates** exposed to MPTP experienced a major loss of neurons in the **substantia nigra** and a reduction in **dopamine**
- in addition, most of these primates developed a Parkinson's disease-like behavioral syndrome; curiously, however, some MPTP monkeys do not develop the parkinsonian symptoms even though their dopamine levels have been depleted
- the behavioral effects of MPTP on **laboratory rodents** proved to be mild, unreliable, and temporary; this difference between primates and rodents emphasizes the importance of a comparative approach to biopsychological research
- use of the MPTP animal model of Parkinson's disease led to the discovery that **deprenyl**, a monoamine agonist and monoamine oxidase (MAO) inhibitor, blocks the effects of MPTP in primates…and more importantly, that deprenyl administration in early Parkinson's patients greatly slows the progression of the disease

Suggested Websites for Lecture 10b:

Animal Models of Parkinson's Disease: *http://darwin.apnet.com/inscight/09301997/grapha.htm*
News on a genetically engineered mouse that resists the pathology associated with Parkinson's Disease.

Squirrels and Strokes: *http://www.sciencenews.org/sn_arc97/12_6_97/bob1.htm*
Insights that hibernating squirrels are giving stroke researchers about cerebral blood flow and brain function.

New Hope for Alzheimer's Patients?
http://www.alzheimersupport.com/library/showarticle.cfm/id/1553

Research using the Transgenic Mouse Model of Alzheimer's Disease to develop a possible vaccine for Alzheimer's Disease.

Lecture 10c

DEGENERATION, REGENERATION, NEUROTRANSPLANTATION AND RECOVERY OF FUNCTION IN THE NERVOUS SYSTEM

Outline

1. Neural Damage: Degeneration, Regeneration, Reorganization and Recovery
   a. Degeneration
   b. Regeneration
   c. Reorganization

2. Neuroplasticity and the Treatment of Nervous System Damage
   a. Blocking Neurodegeneration
   b. Promoting Recovery by Promoting Regeneration
   c. Promoting Recovery by Neurotransplantation
   d. Promoting Recovery by Rehabilitative Training

Lecture Notes

1. **Neural Damage: Degeneration, Regeneration, Reorganization and Recovery** (see Fig. 10.15 – 10.20 in *BIOPSYCHOLOGY;* use *Digital Image Archive Figure CH15F19.BMP - CH15F26.BMP)*

   a. **Degeneration:**

   - a deterioration of the neuron following damage. There are **2 main types:**

      i) **anterograde degeneration** involves **distal segments** of the axon and occurs rapidly following an axotomy; the entire segment of the axon that was separated from the cell body swells and within a few days breaks into fragments.

      ii) **retrograde degeneration** involves changes in the **proximal segments** of the axon from the site of damage back to the soma over a 2-3 day period; if early changes show an increase in the size, the neuron will likely regenerate the axon; if early changes include a decrease in size the entire cell will probably degenerate and die

   - **transneuronal degeneration** is the spread of degeneration from damaged neurons to neurons on which they synapse; **anterograde transneuronal degeneration** is when neurons postsynaptic to the damaged cell are affected; **retrograde transneuronal degeneration** is when neurons that are presynaptic to the damaged cell are affected

   b. **Regeneration:**

   - is a regrowth of the damaged neurons; this occurs more readily in **invertebrates** than in **higher vertebrates**; is hit-or-miss in the **PNS** of mammals, and is almost nonexistent in the **CNS** of adult mammals
   - in mammalian PNS regeneration, regrowth from the **proximal stump** of the damaged neuron begins 2-3 days after damage; if the **myelin sheath** is intact, regrowth may be guided through the myelin sheath and toward the original   target
   - however, if a segment of the nerve has been cut the regenerating axons may grow into incorrect sheaths and thus to **incorrect targets;** or else the axon may grow in a tangled mass without direction

- **collateral sprouting** is the growth of axon branches from adjacent healthy neurons and may occur at the site of degenerating neurons
- **CNS neurons** can regenerate if they are placed in the PNS, whereas **PNS neurons** cannot regenerate in the CNS; the secret to regeneration in the PNS appears to be the Schwann cells that form myelin sheaths in the PNS
- Schwann cells promote regeneration by releasing both **trophic factors** (promote growth) and **cell-adhesion molecules** (guide growing axons to targets)

c. Reorganization

- damage to sensory and motor pathways, the sensory and motor cortexes, and distortion of sensory experiences have all been used to study **neural reorganization** in adult mammals
- for example, Kaas et al., (1990) found that retinal lesions resulted in **new visual receptive fields** in areas of the primary visual cortex that had originally received input from the lesioned areas of **retina.** It was later learned that these changes begin within **minutes** of the retinal lesion!
- in a similar vein, Sanes, Suner & Donoghue (1990) found that transection of the **motor neurons** that controlled the vibrissae muscles of rats produced changes in the associated motor cortex areas to that they came to activate other parts of the face after a **few weeks**
- the reorganization of neural connections is believed to occur via 2 types of changes:

    i) rapid reorganization of neural connections usually results from experience; this is believed to reflect the strengthening of existing connections; and

    ii) gradual reorganization usually results from neural damage; this is believed to reflect the establishment of new connections via collateral sprouting.

- the actual extent of neural reorganization and recovery of function after brain damage remains unclear; it is **difficult to conduct well-controlled studies** on populations of brain-damaged patients, and the nervous system can **compensate** for brain damage in a way that looks like true recovery of function
- **cognitive reserve** (related to education and intelligence) is important in the apparent recovery of cognitive function that is often observed; this seems to be due to the adoption of alternative strategies to solve a problem, rather than true recovery of function
- 2 general conclusions have emerged: 1) **small lesions** are more likely to be associated with recovery of function than large lesions; and 2) recovery of function is more likely in **young patients.**

2. Neuroplasticity and Treatment of Nervous System Damage

- this is currently one of the most active and exciting areas of biopsychology research; the goals are to reduce neurodegeneration or promote neural regeneration in human patients.

a) Blocking Neurodegeneration

- researchers have found that the neurodegeneration normally caused by ischemia can be blocked by administration of viruses that release **apoptosis inhibitor protein;** this blocked the loss of hippocampal cells and poor performance in the Morris water maze that was observed in untreated control rats

a) Promoting Recovery by Promoting Regeneration

- regeneration can be promoted in the CNS; for example, Eitan and colleagues (1994) found that the optic nerve could be induced to regenerate by administering drugs that kill the oligodendrocytes that normally impede regeneration in the CNS; the regenerated nerve produced evoked potentials 6 weeks after the initial injury
- regeneration in the spinal cord has been promoted by transplantation of myelinated PNS nerves across the transection; spinal cord neurons grew through the implanted Schwann cell myelin sheaths and allowed the rats to use their hindquarters

a) Promoting Recovery by Neurotransplantation

- this research has taken 2 different paths, focusing on transplantation of fetal tissue or stem cells

i)   Fetal Tissue Implants:

- based on successful transplants in the **primate MPTP model,** doctors bilaterally implanted **fetal substantia nigra** cells into the **striatum** of Parkinson's patients
- initial reports were promising as many patients showed a reduction of symptoms; however, the results of a subsequent, large-scale **double-blind evaluation** suggests that as many as 15% of patients showing an initial positive response to the transplanted tissue develop **side effects** such as uncontrollable writhing and chewing movements

ii) Stem Cell Transplants:

- this works is currently in its **early stages**
- recall that stem cells are **pluripotent** (can develop into many different types of mature cells).
- stem cell researchers are trying to use stem cell transplants to correct brain damage; for example, McDonald and colleagues found that stem cells injected into the area of a spinal cord transection developed into neurons and glial cells in the area of the transection; their functionality is evidenced by the fact that the formerly paraplegic rats were able to support their own weight and eventually walk

a) Promotion of Recovery by Rehabilitative Training:

- it has become clear that experience can facilitate the functional reorganization of the CNS following damage
- for example, small **strokes** often produce a **core of damage**, which is followed by a gradually expanding loss of function around this core. This latter loss can be reduced in motor cortex by **rehabilitative training;** recovery of function following damage to the hand area of motor cortex in primates is facilitated if the monkeys engage in **manual tasks** during their recuperation; there is less loss of tissue and greater recovery of manual dexterity.
- following **spinal cord injury** in humans, people receiving rehabilitative training showed greater recovery of function (walking) than people that simply received conventional physiotherapy.
- about 50% of amputees suffer from **phantom limb pain;** surgical interventions are notoriously poor at treating such pain, but it can be reduced by encouraging **reorganization** of the areas of **somatosensory cortex** that previously innervated the amputated limb.

Suggested Websites for Lecture 10c:

> **Transplantation in the CNS:** *http://www.sciencedaily.com/releases/2001/02/010216081637.htm*
> Summary from the Science Daily online e-zine; review of use of stem cells in treatment of brain injuries.

> **Stem Cells in the Brain:** *http://www.princeton.edu/pr/pwb/99/0405/brain.htm*
> From Princeton University's Weekly Bulletin, a look at Dr. Elizabeth Gould's work on the role of stem cells in neural development and recovery from brain damage.

IM-AT-A-GLANCE: Chapter 11. Learning, Memory and Amnesia:
How Your Brain Stores Information

Detailed Outline	Print Supplements	Media Supplements	Professor's Notes
Chapter 11. Learning, Memory & Amnesia: How Your Brain Stores Information, pp. 268-296	**Instructor's Manual for** *BIOPSYCHOLOGY,* *Lecture 11a and* *Lecture 11b*	***Beyond the Brain & Behavior CD for* BIOPSYCHOLOGY:** *My Tumor and Welcome To It* Module	
11.1 Amnesic Effects of Bilateral Medial Temporal Lobectomy	**Test Bank for** *BIOPSYCHOLOGY,* *Chapter 11*	*Practice Tests for Chapter 11*	
11.2 Amnesia of Korsakoff's Syndrome	**Study Guide for** *BIOPSYCHOLOGY,*	*Hard Copy for Chapter 11*	
11.3 Amnesia of Alzheimer's Disease	*Chapter 11*	*Electronic Flashcards for Chapter 11*	
11.4 Amnesia After Concussion: Evidence for Consolidation	**Transparencies for Physiological Psychology:** *XI. Learning, Memory and Neural Plasticity*	**Digital Image Archive, PowerPoint Presentation and Bitmap Images for** *BIOPSYCHOLOGY:* Chapter 14 Chapter 15	
11.5 Neuroanatomy of Object-Recognition Memory		**Biological Psychology Video, Segment 12.** *Memory*	
11.6 The Hippocampus and Memory for Spatial Location			
11.7 Where Are Memories Stored?			
11.8 Synaptic Mechanisms of Learning & Memory			
11.9 Conclusion: Infantile Amnesia and The Biopsychologist Who Remembered H.M.			

Lecture 11a

THE NEUROPSYCHOLOGY OF MEMORY

Outline

1. Amnesic Effects of Bilateral Medial Temporal Lobectomy

   a. The Case of H.M.
   b. H.M.'s Memory Deficits
   c. Impact of H.M.'s Case
   d. Medial Temporal Lobe Amnesia
   e. The Case of R.B.

2. Korsakoff's Amnesia

3. Alzheimer's Disease

4. Posttraumatic Amnesia

Lecture Notes

- **learning** deals with how experience changes the brain and **memory** refers to how these changes are stored and later reactivated
- we have learned much about the neural mechanisms of memory by studying amnesic patients

1. Amnesic Effects of Bilateral Medial Temporal Lobectomy (see Fig. 11.1 – 11.5 in *BIOPSYCHOLOGY*; use *Digital Image Archive Figure CH14F02.BMP, CH14F03.BMP, CH14F06.BMP,* and *CH14F07.BMP;* use *Biological Psychology Video, Segment 12. Memory)*

a. The Case of H.M.

- H.M. suffered from severe, intractable epilepsy; he seemed to have **epileptic foci** in both **medial temporal lobes**
- because unilateral medial temporal lobectomy had proven successful in patients with one focus, a **bilateral medial temporal lobectomy** was prescribed for H.M.; this included the removal of the **hippocampus** and **amygdala**
- in some respects, the operation was a success: HM's convulsions were reduced in severity and frequency, his I.Q. increased from about 104 to about 118, and he remained an emotionally stable individual with generally superior psychological abilities
- there is one exception to this otherwise rosy picture…HM suffered from devastating amnesia as a result of his operation

b. H.M.'s memory deficits

- H.M. has minor **retrograde amnesia** (amnesia for events before his surgery) for events of the 2 years preceding the surgery
- he has normal memory for remote events and normal **short-term memory** (his digit span is about 6)
- however, he cannot form long-term memories for events that occurred after his surgery (**anterograde amnesia**), for example he has no memory of his new home, his new job, or new friends
- at first, it was assumed that H.M. could not form long-term memories at all, but objective testing revealed that H.M. can demonstrate his retention of certain types of tasks by his improved performance on them, although he has **no conscious recollection** of previously practicing them

- H.M.'s deficits can be described in terms of his performance on six objective tests of memory:

    i)   **Digit Span +1 Test:** after 25 trials with the same series of digits, he could do only 7 digits, just one more than his normal memory span

    ii)   **Block-Tapping Memory-Span Test:** his block-tapping memory-span was normal; but he could not extend it, even by one, when the same sequence was repeated for 12 trials

    iii)   **Mirror-Drawing Test:** he displayed substantial savings with no conscious recall of previous practice

    iv)   **Rotary-Pursuit Test:** he displayed substantial savings with no conscious recall of previous practice

    v)   **Incomplete-Pictures Test:** after seeing 5 sets of 20 line drawings of varying completeness, he displayed substantial savings with no conscious recall of the drawings

    vi)   **Pavlovian Conditioning:** tones and a puff of air to the eye were presented to H.M.; he blinked in response; two years later he retained this conditioned pairing almost perfectly although he had no conscious awareness of his previous training

c.   Impact of H.M.'s Case

- H.M.'s case had the following significant influences on the study of memory:

    i)   it showed that the medial temporal lobes are important to mnemonic functions;

    ii)   it challenged the view that mnemonic functions are diffusely represented throughout the brain

    iii)   it renewed efforts to relate specific brain structures to specific mnemonic processes

    iv)   it supported the theory that there is a different mode of storage for **short-term** and **long-term** memories;

    v)   H.M.'s case provided the first evidence that **implicit memory** could survive in the absence of **explicit memory;**

d.   Medial Temporal Lobe Amnesia

- H.M.'s ability to form implicit, but not explicit, long-term memories is often seen in cases of medial temporal lobe amnesia, as well as other amnesic disorders
- **repetition priming tests** are used to assess implicit memory; patients are shown a list of words and sometime later they are shown a series of word fragments and asked to complete the words. Amnesic patients do as well on this task as control subjects, even though they do not remember ever seeing the original list of words.
- recent research has suggested that problems with **episodic memory** (memories for the events of one's own life) are more common than problems with **semantic memory** (memories for general facts or information) in patients suffering from medial temporal lobe amnesia
- the fact that implicit memories are intact while explicit memories are compromised in patients suffering from medial temporal lobe amnesia raises the question "Why do we have 2 memory systems…one conscious, and the other unconscious?"
- the answer seems to be **flexibility;** implicit memories do not transfer well to different contexts, whereas explicit memories can.

e.   The Case of R.B.

- R.B. suffered **ischemia**-produced brain damage during heart surgery; subsequently, R.B. displayed a pattern of amnesic deficits similar to, although less severe than, that of H.M.
- shortly after testing, R.B. died and postmortem examination revealed damage to the **pyramidal cell layer** of the **CA1 hippocampal subfield,** but no other obvious damage
- this supported the original hypothesis that H.M.'s deficits were attributable to his hippocampal damage, rather than to damage to other medial-temporal-lobe structures…as we shall see, however, this may not be the case

2. Korsakoff's Amnesia

- individuals who chronically consume alcohol develop a pattern of behavioral disorders commonly referred to as **Korsakoff's syndrome**
- in addition to severe **anterograde amnesia**, Korsakoff patients suffer from a severe **retrograde amnesia**
- although their retrograde amnesia is more severe for recent memories, it also affects their memory for events occurring many years before the diagnosis of their case (i.e., for remote events)
- this temporal gradient is usually assumed to reflect a gradient of retrograde amnesia, however, it could reflect the insidious development of anterograde deficits prior to diagnosis--or a combination of both
- the brain damage associated with Korsakoff's amnesia is diffuse, but the amnesia is usually attributed to medial diencephalic damage, particularly to the **mediodorsal nuclei of the thalamus**
- support for the role of diencephalic structures in mnemonic function comes from the patient N.A.
- N.A. was in the air force; one day, he was accidentally stabbed in the brain through the right nostril by a friend with a fencing foil; he suffered both retrograde and anterograde amnesia
- the foil penetrated the **cribriform plate; a** subsequent MRI revealed extensive damage in medial diencephalon, including the **mediodorsal thalamic nuclei** and the **mammillary bodies**
- despite this evidence, it is unlikely that Korsakoff's amnesia is due to damage to any single brain region

3. Alzheimer's Disease

- this is a major cause of amnesia; the first symptom is often a mild loss of memory
- the disease is progressive; eventually, the dementia becomes severe enough to complete incapacitate the patient
- considerable attention has been focused on **predementia Alzheimer's patients;** in addition to both anterograde and retrograde amnesia, these patients often display deficits in short-term memory and some forms of implicit memory (those involving verbal or perceptual material, but not sensorimotor learning)
- pathological changes include reduced levels of the neurotransmitter **acetylcholine**; these changes suggested that acetylcholine plays a role in the amnesia observed in Alzheimer's patients

4. Posttraumatic Amnesia *((see Fig. 11.6 – 11.8 in* **BIOPSYCHOLOGY;** *use Digital Image Archive Figure CH14F08.BMP)*

- blows to the head can lead to a disturbance of consciousness (**concussion**), a complete loss of consciousness (**coma),** and amnesia; the memory loss attributable to a nonpenetrating blow to the head is called **posttraumatic amnesia**
- patients with posttraumatic amnesia generally have both anterograde and retrograde amnesia; in general, the anterograde amnesia is longer than the period of coma that produced it, while the duration of the coma lasts longer than the period of retrograde amnesia that it produced
- the retrograde amnesia seen after concussion or coma is typically worse for the most recent memories; this led to the suggestion that older memory are stored in a more permanent form through the process of **consolidation**
- **electroconvulsive shock (ECS)** has been used to study the process of consolidation; this has led to the belief that consolidation is a long-term process that may take years to complete

Suggested Websites for Lecture 11a:

The Hippocampus: *http://thalamus.wustl.edu/course/limbic.html*
From Washington University; see the second half of this page for some great figures (including effects of hypoxia on the CA1 cells of the hippocampal formation) and text.

Concussions: *http://www.miaims.missouri.edu/~neuromedicine/concussion.shtml*
From the University of Missouri's Health Sciences Center, a review of the causes and signs of concussion.

Lecture 11b
Object Recognition, Spatial Memory, and LTP

Outline

1. Inadequacy of Early Animal Models of Amnesia

2. Studying Object Recognition in Animals: Nonrecurring-Items Delayed Nonmatching-to-Sample
    a. Monkeys
    b. Rats

3. The Use of Animal Models to Study the Neural Bases of Memory
    a. Which Structures Contribute to Medial-Temporal-Lobe Amnesia?
    b. The Hippocampus and Memory for Spatial Location
    c. Theories of Hippocampal Function

4. Where Are Memories Stored?

5. Synaptic Mechanisms of Learning & Memory

Lecture Notes

1. Inadequacy of Early Animal Models of Amnesia

-   early attempts to develop an animal model of medial temporal lobe amnesia were largely unsuccessful
-   in part, this was because researchers did not know that H.M.'s amnesia was restricted to explicit long-term memory…and most animal memory tests of the time focused on tests of implicit memory
-   problems developing an animal model of medial temporal lobe epilepsy were also due to the fact that researcher's attention focused almost entirely on the hippocampus…thus ignoring contributions from other structures that were damaged during H.M.'s surgery

2. A New Paradigm to Assess Memory in Animals: The Delayed Nonmatching-to-Sample Test (see Fig. 11.9 – 11.14 in *BIOPSYCHOLOGY;* use *Digital Image Archive Figure CH14F11.BMP, CH14F13.BMP,* and *CH14F15.BMP)*

-   a good animal model of H.M.'s amnesic condition emerged in the 1970's with the development of the primate **delayed nonmatching-to-sample task (DNMTS)**

a. Monkeys
-   on each trial in the DNMTS, a monkey is presented with a distinct sample object; under the object is some food
-   after a delay, the monkey is presented with two objects…the sample object and a novel object
-   the monkey's task is to select the novel object; it must remember the sample object so that it can obtain the food from beneath the novel object on the test portion of the trial
-   medial temporal lobe damage makes this task very difficult if there is any kind of a delay between presentation of the sample object and the presentation of the two objects on the test trial

b. Rats
-   Mumby and Pinel (1990) developed a version of the nonmatching-to-sample paradigm for rats
-   in the Mumby box, a rat runs to one end of a straight alley and pushes a sample object aside to get a morsel of food
-   the sample is removed and the rat is kept in that end by an opaque door until the appropriate delay has passed; the door is then raised and the animal must run to the two objects at the other end and push aside the novel object to obtain the morsel beneath it
-   then the rat runs to the center of the box; doors to prevent it from approaching the ends of the alley are closed, and the rat is in a position to begin the next trial

- remarkably, the performance of rats is not substantially different from that of monkeys at retention intervals of up to 5 minutes

3. The Use of Animal Models to Study the Neural Bases of Memory (see Fig. 11.15 in *BIOPSYCHOLOGY*; use *Digital Image Archive Figure CH14F17.BMP)*

a. Which Structures Contribute to Medial-Temporal-Lobe Amnesia?

- in the early 1990's, researchers began to question the role of the hippocampus in the memory deficits observed following medial temporal lobectomy.
- these researchers noted that hippocampal surgery in primates usually involved damage to **overlying cortical structures** as well; in particular, the possible contribution of the **rhinal cortex** and **amygdala** was examined
- researchers found that lesions of the hippocampus that do not damage overlying cortex produce only mild deficits in the DNMTS test; lesions restricted to the amygdala had no effect at all; and, lesions of rhinal cortex that do not damage the hippocampus produce major deficits
- these data cast into doubt the conclusions reached based on the **ischemic patient R.B.,** who displayed amnesia attributed to damage to the **CA1 cell subfield** of the hippocampus. How could such discrete damage produce amnesia, when animal studies suggested that lesioning the entire hippocampus had little effect on DNMTS unless the overlying cortex was also disturbed?
- surprisingly, Mumby and his colleagues found that ischemia-induced amnesia in the DNMTS test in rats can be *blocked* by large bilateral hippocampectomy…suggesting that the hippocampal damage displayed by R.B. did not contribute significantly to his amnesia!
- according to Mumby and colleagues explanation for this apparent mystery, ischemia produces **hyperactivity** in the CA1 region of the hippocampus; this hyperactivity damages neurons in the terminal fields of the CA1 cells, possibly by excessive release of **excitatory amino acid transmitters**

b. Hippocampus and Memory for Spatial Location

- although the hippocampus may not be critical to the performance of the DNMTS test, it does appear to be involved in the mediation of **spatial memory**
- two techniques are widely used to test spatial memory

  i) the **Morris water maze test** requires rats to learn the location of an invisible stationary platform and find it when swimming in opaque (usually milk-white) water; rats with hippocampal lesions have great difficulty with this task whereas control rats without hippocampal damage easily learn the task

  ii) in the **radial arm maze test**, there is a central chamber with as many as 8 alleys or "arms" radiating from it. During each test, a few of the 8 arms of the apparatus are baited with some kind of reward; intact rats learn to visit only the baited arms (this is referred to as **reference memory**); rats with hippocampal lesions show deficits in reference memory in that they do not exclusively visit baited arms. In addition, they show deficits in **working memory** as they repeatedly visit unbaited arms during each test

- further evidence for the role of the hippocampus in spatial memory comes from the existence of hippocampal **place cells**, first identified in rats by O'Keefe and Dostrovsky (1971); these cells fired when a rat is placed in a specific location, but only after the rat becomes familiar with that location
- comparative research has revealed that the hippocampus plays a role in the spatial memory of many different species
- for example, Sherry and his colleagues (1992) have reported that **food-caching birds** tend to have larger hippocampi than noncaching species

c. Theories of Hippocampal Function

- there are many theories that attempt to account for the role of the hippocampus in memory; these include:

    i) Okeefe & Nadels's **cognitive map theory** (the hippocampus constructs maps of the external world based on the relationships between external landmarks and objects);
    ii) Rudy & Sutherland's **configural association theory** (the hippocampus organizes and retains the behavioral significance of combinations of stimuli and the context that they are presented in, but not the individual stimuli themselves); and
    iii) Brown & Aggleton's **spatial arrangement theory** (the hippocampus is involved in recognizing spatial arrangements between objects, but not the objects themselves)

4. Where Are Memories Stored? (see Fig. 11.16 in *BIOPSYCHOLOGY;* use *Digital Image Archive Figure CH14F19.BMP)*

- the following regions are also believed to play a role in memory storage:

    i) **inferotemporal cortex:** as an area of **secondary sensory cortex,** this area is believed to play a role in the storage of **long-term visual memories**
    ii) **amygdala:** this area is involved in memories for the **emotional significance** of an event; lesions here impair **fear conditioning** or **startle responses**
    iii) **prefrontal cortex:** damage in this area does not produce a gross memory defect, but it does impair memory for **temporal order** of events and also **working memory**
    iv) **cerebellum and striatum:** these areas are involved in implicit memories of sensorimotor learning; the role of the cerebellum in the **conditioned eyeblink response** has been intensely studied, and the striatum is believed to be involved in **habit learning**

5. Synaptic Mechanisms of Learning & Memory Test (see Fig. 11.17 – 11.20 in *BIOPSYCHOLOGY;* use *Digital Image Archive Figure CH15F15.BMP, CH15F16.BMP,* and *CH15F18.BMP)*

Long-Term Potentiation

- LTP is interesting because it is the kind of change that was postulated by Hebb in 1949 to underlie memory
- in an LTP experiment, a brief period of **intense high-frequency stimulation** enhances the subsequent response of postsynaptic neurons to low-intensity stimulation of the presynaptic neurons. This enhancement can last for weeks depending on the number, duration, frequency, and intensity of the inducing stimulations
- LTP is often studied in the **hippocampal-slice preparation;** for example, LTP has frequently been studied in terms of changes in the response of neurons in the **granule-cell layer** of the **hippocampal dentate gyrus** following intense high-frequency **perforant path** stimulation
- LTP has 2 qualities that fit with the type of synaptic changes that Hebb suggested would underlie learning: it is reasonably permanent, and it occurs only when both the presynaptic and the postsynaptic neurons were simultaneously active. This need for **co-occurrence** of activation is called **Hebb's postulate for learning.**
- the **NMDA** (N-methyl-D-aspartate) **glutamate** receptor appears to mediate many forms of hippocampal LTP; interestingly, NMDA-mediated activation of postsynaptic neurons requires that the postsynaptic cell already be depolarized by concurrent activation by non-NMDA receptors; this requirement for **co-occurrence of activity** provides further support for Hebb's postulate and the putative role of LTP in learning.
- full activation of NMDA receptors allows Ca^{2+} ions to enter postsynaptic neurons; this Ca^{2+} influx is believed to activate **protein kinases** that are responsible for the induction of LTP

- it is unclear whether maintenance and expression of LTP are due to **presynaptic** or **postsynaptic** changes; however some research has offered clues:

    1) Harris & Kater (1994) have found that the LTP develops only at **specific presynaptic inputs** (that are active during periods of postsynaptic depolarization) is attributable to calcium entering only those **dendritic spines** that are activated during the high-frequency stimulation.

    2) Nguyen, Abel & Kandell (1994) have found that **blocking protein synthesis** immediately after the administration of high-frequency stimulation has no effect on the maintenance of LTP for one or two hours, but blocks its maintenance for longer periods

    3) Several researchers have suggested that **nitric oxide** (NO), a **soluble gas neurotransmitter** that is produced by postsynaptic neurons during periods of activation, may serve as the signal that passes from the postsynaptic neuron back to the presynaptic neuron to induce the changes that underlie the maintenance of LTP.

    4) Other researchers have documented increases in the **number of s**ynapses that exist between pre- and postsynaptic neurons following the induction of LTP.

- LTP is one of the most intensely studied phenomena in biological psychology; many different forms of LTP have been discovered; the major goal of psychological research is to understand how these different forms of synaptic plasticity contribute to learning and memory.

Suggested Websites for Lecture 11b:

The Hippocampus: *http://thalamus.wustl.edu/course/limbic.html*
> From Washington University's Neuroscience tutorial; see the second half of this page for anatomical figures (including effects of hypoxia on the CA1 cells of the hippocampal formation) and text discussing the role of the hippocampus in memory. For a sheep's brain-based dissection of the anatomy of memory, see:

> *http://www.exploratorium.edu/memory/braindissection/index.html*

Prefrontal Cortex: *http://www.sciam.com/0897issue/0897trends.html*
> From Scientific American, an overview of the role of the prefrontal cortex in memory function; good figures and links to other sites.

Tests of Memory: *http://olias.arc.nasa.gov/cognition/tutorials/index.html*
> From NASA's Ames Research Center, five tests of memory function.

IM-AT-A-GLANCE: Chapter 12. Hunger, Eating, and Health:
Why Do Many People Eat Too Much?

Detailed Outline	Print Supplements	Media Supplements	Professor's Notes
Chapter 12. Hunger, Eating, & Health: Why Do Many People Eat Too Much? pp. 297-323 12.1 Digestion & Energy Flow 12.2 Theories of Hunger & Eating: Set Points v. Positive Incentives 12.3 Factors That Determine What, When & How Much We Eat 12.4 Physiological Research on Hunger & Satiety 12.5 Body Weight Regulation: Set Points v. Settling Points 12.6 Human Obesity 12.7 Anorexia Nervosa	**Instructor's Manual for** *BIOPSYCHOLOGY,* *Lecture 12a and Lecture 12b* **Test Bank for** *BIOPSYCHOLOGY,* *Chapter 12* **Study Guide for** *BIOPSYCHOLOGY,* *Chapter 12* **Transparencies for Physiological Psychology:** *VII. Feeding*	*Beyond the Brain & Behavior CD for* **BIOPSYCHOLOGY:** *Thinking About Hunger* module; *Leaky Barrel* module *Practice Tests for Chapter 12* *Hard Copy for Chapter 12* *Electronic Flashcards for Chapter 12* **Digital Image Archive, PowerPoint Presentation and Bitmap Images for** *BIOPSYCHOLOGY:* *Chapter 10*	

Lecture 12a

SET POINTS VERSUS POSITIVE INCENTIVES...
WHAT, WHEN AND HOW MUCH WE EAT

Outline:

1.   Digestion and Energy Flow

2.   Set-Point Theories v. Positive-Incentive Theories of Hunger and Eating
     a. Setpoint Theories
     b. Positive-Incentive Theories

3.   Factors That Determine What, When and How Much We Eat
     a.   What We Eat
     b.   When We Eat
     c.   How Much We Eat

4.   Physiological Research on Hunger and Satiety
     a.   Hypothalamic Hunger and Satiety Centers
     b.   The GI Tract and Satiety
     c.   Satiety Peptides

Lecture Notes

1.   **Digestion & Energy Flow** (see Fig. 12.1 – 12.3 in *BIOPSYCHOLOGY;* use *Digital Image Archive Figure CH10F01.BMP* and *CH10F03.BMP;* use *Beyond the Brain and Behavior CD,* *Thinking About Hunger module*)

     -   **digestion** is the gastrointestinal process of breaking down food and absorbing its constituents into the body
     -   the primary purpose of eating is to supply the body with the energy that it needs to survive
     -   energy is available in three forms (1) **lipids** (fats), (2) **proteins** (broken into amino acids), and (3) **glucose** (simple sugar byproducts of carbohydrates)
     -   energy is usually stored in the form of **fat**
     -   energy metabolism occurs in three phases:

          i)   the **cephalic** phase: this is a preparatory phase; it begins with the sight, smell of even thought of food; **insulin** is released by the pancreas to promote glucose use and storage
          ii)   the **absorptive** phase: this is when energy is absorbed into the bloodstream; **insulin** is released by the pancreas to promote glucose use and storage
          iii)   the **fasting** phase: this is when body utilizes energy stores; **glucagons** is released by the pancreas to promote the use of **free fatty acids** and **ketones** by the body

2.   **Set Point v. Positive Incentive Theories of Eating** (see Fig. 12.4 in *BIOPSYCHOLOGY;* use *Digital Image Archive Figure CH10F04.BMP;* use *Beyond the Brain and Behavior CD,* *Thinking About Hunger module*)

     a.   **Set Point Theories**

          -   research on feeding has been heavily influenced by the idea of a feeding **set-point,** based around the idea of a homeostatic, negative feedback system regulating feeding
          -   research on feeding has been strongly influenced by the idea that feeding is controlled by deviations from two different **set points:** a set point for **blood glucose (short-term regulation)** and a set point for **body fat (long-term regulation)**

- there are many problems with set-point models of feeding: they cannot explain the current epidemic of **eating disorders** in our society; they are inconsistent with current ideas about **evolutionary pressures** related to eating; eating does not seem to be sensitive to changes in **body fat** or the **caloric status** of an individual prior to a meal; and they fail to recognize the role that factors like **taste, learning** or **social factors** play in eating.

b. Positive Incentive Theories

- developed in response to shortcomings with set-point theories of feeding; positive incentive theories emphasize the idea that animals eat not because of deviations from some internal energy set-point but because of the anticipated pleasure of eating.
- in this sense, feeding is a lot like sexual behavior; we do it because we crave it, not because we are trying to match a set-point
- according to positive incentive theories, animals eat in response to a host of factors: preferred flavors; past experiences with a food; the time since your last meal; whether or not other people are eating; etc.

3. Factors That Determine What, When & How Much We Eat (see Fig. 12.5 and Fig. 12.6 in *BIOPSYCHOLOGY;* use *Digital Image Archive Figure CH10F05.BMP)*

a. What We Eat

- in general animals are born with a preference for sweet and salty tastes and with an aversion to bitter tastes
- but they learn to avoid any taste followed by illness (**conditioned taste aversion**) or to prefer tastes that improve their health (**conditioned taste preference**)
- humans and other animals learn to prefer flavors associated with mother's milk, or foods that they see their conspecifics eating
- when an animal is **sodium deficient,** it develops a craving for sodium salt; however, when it becomes deficient in a vitamin or another mineral it must learn to consume foods that are rich in the missing nutrient. This becomes a problem when an animal is faced with a multitude of food possibilities...as humans often are.
- for example, when **thiamin** (Vitamin B_1) deficient rats were offered two different diets, one of which had thiamin, within a few days all preferred the thiamin diet; however, when they were offered 10 new diets, few learned to consume the one with thiamin

b. When We Eat

- when food is readily available, most mammals eat **many small meals** a day
- by contrast, most humans choose to eat a **few large meals** at regular times; in fact, many people feel ill if they miss a scheduled meal
- this is due to the fact that animals will enter the cephalic phase of feeding as the mealtime approaches; the malaise that you feel occurs when insulin is released and blood glucose levels fall in expectation of the coming meal
- recent research by Weingarten and his colleagues suggests that nondeprived humans and animals learn to become hungry when they are used to eating, not when they have an energy deficit-- nondeprived humans and animals do not normally have energy deficits when they begin meals
- Weingarten fed deprived rats 6 small meals per day of a highly palatable liquid diet at irregular intervals for 11 days; a buzzer-and-light conditional stimulus came on before each meal and stayed on during it
- next, Weingarten gave these same rats continuous access to the palatable liquid diet; despite the fact that they consumed large quantities of the liquid diet throughout the day, each time the buzzer and light were presented the rats consumed a meal

c. How Much We Eat

- **satiety signals** based on volume of food intake and its **nutritive density** influence how much we eat; to a point, animals will adjust their eating to keep food intake and body weight stable
- **sham eating** studies indicate that signals from the gut or blood are not necessary to terminate eating; in sham eating studies, food is chewed and swallowed but it leaves the body before it enters the stomach
- **set-point theory** suggests that sham-eaten meals should be huge, as there cannot be a satiety signal generated as food intake meets caloric requirements; that is not the case, as the size of these meals seems to depend more on an animals previous experience with the food than with its immediate effects on the body
- eating a small amount of food prior to a meal often increases the size of that meal; this is known as the **appetizer effect**
- eating in the company of others often influences the size of the meal that is eaten
- the variety of foods available at a meal also influences meal size; the greater the variety, the more food that is eaten. This is due to **sensory-specific satiety**…this is one reason why body weight tends to increase when a human being or other animal is faced with a **cafeteria-style diet**

4. **Physiological Research on Hunger and Satiety** (see Fig. 12.7 – Fig. 12.12 in *BIOPSYCHOLOGY;* use *Digital Image Archive Figure CH10F08.BMP, CH10F10.BMP* and *CH10F12.BMP*)

a. Hypothalamic Hunger and Satiety Centers

- in the 1950's, studies in which various areas of the rat hypothalamus were lesioned or stimulated seemed to suggest that it contained the hypothesized **hunger** and **satiety centers**
- large bilateral lesions of the **ventromedial hypothalamus (VMH)** produced **hyperphagia** and gross obesity; after the lesion, the rats were extremely hyperphagic and gained weight rapidly (**dynamic phase**); after several weeks hyperphagia was only slight and a new, very high body weight was maintained (**static phase**)
- by contrast, large bilateral lesions of the **lateral hypothalamus (LH)** rendered rats **aphagic** and **adipsic;** if force fed and then maintained on highly palatable wet diets, they eventually recovered to the point that they could maintain themselves on laboratory chow and water
- although the idea of **VMH satiety** and **LH feeding centers** in the brain was attractive, it has proven to be **false**
- for example, it turns out that the hypothalamus is primarily involved in **energy metabolism,** not food intake. VMH lesions increase blood insulin levels; this increases the production of body fat and forces animals to eat more in order to maintain glucose blood levels for their immediate energy requirements.
- In addition, VMH lesions are not due to damage to the VMH itself, but instead to damage to the **ventral noradrenergic bundle** or the axons of the **paraventricular nucleus of the hypothalamus**

b. The GI Tract and Satiety

- the first influential study of the physiological basis of hunger was conducted in 1912 by **Canon and Washburn**; Washburn swallowed a balloon on the end of a thin tube, the balloon was partially inflated, and a pressure gauge was attached to the other end of the tube
- each time that he had a large stomach contraction, Washburn reported a pang of hunger; this led to the view that stomach contractions are a major factor in hunger.
- the finding that animals whose stomachs had been completely removed ate enough to maintain their body weights discredited this view; in addition, people with no stomachs report feeling hungry and maintain their body weights; they eat less per meal, but they eat more meals
- in the 1980's, Koopmans has used a **second-stomach preparation** to implicate the gut in feeding behavior; rats who have had a second stomach implanted into their peritoneum eat less when the second stomach is loaded with food, even though the stomach is not innervated nor are the nutrients able to be absorbed into the bloodstream.

c. Satiety Peptides

- there is considerable evidence that **peptides** released by the gut can serve as satiety signals in the brain; for example, **CCK, bombesin, glucagons** and **somatostatin** all appear to reduce food intake, while **Neuropeptide Y** and **galanin** appear to increase appetite
- the monoamine transmitter **serotonin** is also a potent satiety signal

Suggested Websites for Lecture 12a:

The Hypothalamus: *http://thalamus.wustl.edu/course/hypoANS.html*
>   From the Neuroscience Tutorial at Washington University's School of Medicine, a text-and-figure review of the anatomy, physiology, and function of the hypothalamus.

The Digestive System: *http://www.niddk.nih.gov/health/digest/pubs/digesyst/newdiges.htm*
>   From the National Digestive Diseases Information Clearinghouse, a simple explanation of the dynamics of digestion.

Lecture 12b

HUNGER, SATIETY, AND EATING DISORDERS

Outline:

1. Body Weight Regulation: Set-Points versus Settling Points
   a. Problems with Set-Point Theories
   b. Body Weight Regulation and Settling Point Models

2. Human Obesity
   a. Why Do Only Some People Become Obese?
   b. Physiological Factors in Obesity

3. Anorexia Nervosa

Lecture Notes

1. Body Weight Regulation: Set Points versus Settling Points (see Fig. 12.13 and 12.14 in
   BIOPSYCHOLOGY; use *Digital Image Archive Figure CH10F14.BMP;* use *Beyond the Brain and Behavior CD,* Leaky Barrel module)

a. Problems with Set-Point Theories

- set point theories cannot account for the large **changes in body weight** that are common in adults, or the wave of **obesity** that is currently sweeping fast-food societies
- set point theories cannot account for the fact that animals who eat a free-feeding diet are typically **less healthy** than animals on a calorie-restricted diet; in both humans and animals, those who eat less have **greater longevity** and less likelihood of a variety of diseases
- the enhanced health of animals maintained on a calorie-restricted diet are not related to a decrease in body fat; rather, it is believed that a by-product of energy metabolism accumulates in cells and accelerates the rate of aging and it attendant health problems
- set-point theory cannot account for the fact that the body seems to control its fats levels by **altering its metabolism** rather than its food intake
- the mechanism for this control is called **diet-induced thermogenesis;** increases in body fat increase body temperature, which leads to increased food intake so that the body temperature can be maintained

b. Body Weight Regulation and Settling Point Models

- the inability of set-point theories to accurately describe feeding behavior and body weight has led researchers to consider the idea that body weight tends to drift around a natural **settling point,** or level at which all of the various factors that influence food intake and energy expenditure achieve a **balance**
- from this perspective, body weight is **stable** as long as there are no **long-term changes** in the factors that influence it
- the **leaky-barrel analogy** illustrates the ideas behind a **settling-point theory** of body weight regulation
- according to settling point models, the stability of body weight is a function of the stability of the various factors that influence energy intake and output; if these are changed, their impact is limited by **negative feedback**
- the strength of this model is that it accounts for the **homeostasis** of body weight without having to postulate a fixed set point, and it can also account for instances in which there are long-term changes in body weight, which a strict set-point model cannot
- the most significant aspect of a settling-point based model of food intake is that it better describes what we know about the regulation of food intake and body weight

2. Human Obesity

a. Why Do Only Some People Become Obese?

- rates of obesity have doubled in the last century; this increased incidence represents a significant health problem in many "fast-food" societies.
- one reason why obesity has become so common is that **evolution** has led to animals to prefer high-calorie foods; to eat to maximum capacity; to store as much energy as possible as fat; and to use calories as efficiently as possible. However, this pattern of ingestion is **not adaptive** in a setting in which food shortages are rare and highly palatable food is easily available.
- in addition, **social factors** have encouraged humans tend to eat at set times rather than when we are hungry, and to eat in a way that maximizes our food intake
- all of these factors lead humans to appallingly high levels of food intake…and thus, to increased incidence of obesity in many societies
- other factors help to determine whether a given individual will become obese; these include an individual's unique food preferences; the role of **social factors** in an individual's feeding patterns; differences in **basal metabolism;** differences in **energy expenditures;** and differences in **nonexercise activity thermogenesis (NEAT)**
- from the perspective of settling-point models of weight regulation, weight-loss programs are largely unsuccessful because once the program ends, and an individual resumes the lifestyle factors that initially determined their weight, their eating habits and energy expenditures will lead to their body weight returning to pre-diet levels
- increased exercise by itself is an efficient means of weight loss because **physical activity** normally accounts for just a small amount of a person's total caloric expenditures
- the key to weight loss is a **permanent change** in lifestyle

b. Physiological Factors in Obesity

- in the early 1950's, a spontaneous mutation produced a strain of genetically obese mice called **ob/ob mice;** these mice eat more than normal, weigh 3 times as much as a normal mouse, store fat more effectively than normal mice, and burn fat more efficiently.
- researchers in the 1990's found that these mice cannot produce **leptin,** a hormone produced by fat cells that appears to serve as a **negative feedback signal** for fat deposition in the body. Leptin levels are positively correlated with fat deposits in humans; low doses of leptin reduce eating and body fat in mice; and there are leptin receptors in the brain.
- unfortunately, most humans have high circulating levels of leptin and leptin injection do not reliably reduce body fat in obese humans. Thus, other feedback signals must also be involved in the control of eating in humans.
- these signals include **insulin**; it is also positively correlated with body fat, there are insulin receptors in the brain, and low doses of insulin injected in the brains of lab animals reduces eating and body weight. Furthermore, **knockout mice** that lack the gene for insulin receptors in the brain are fatter than normal mice.
- there is also considerable interest in developing **serotonergic agonists** that suppress appetite without the side effects seen with conventional serotonin agonists.

2. Anorexia Nervosa

- anorexia nervosa is a disorder of **underconsumption of food**; about 2.5% of the North American student population has the disorder, with the majority of patients being female
- anorexics eat so little that they experience **health-threatening weight loss;** in about half of patients with anorexia, binge eating is followed by purging by vomiting or laxatives.
- **bulimia nervosa** is a related condition in which individuals binge-eat and purge in the absence of extreme weight loss

- in many cases, people who develop anorexia begin by trying to maintain a strict diet; traditionally, researchers have thought that this was because such people had managed to overcome the natural attraction that people feel for food.
- an alternative is suggested by a **positive-incentive** model of eating and weight control. From this perspective, **eating** food is not a positive incentive for anorexics even though they are essentially starving themselves…thus, there is no motivation for them to eat.
- this stands in stark contrast to the normal response to starvation, which greatly increases the positive incentive qualities of food.
- one explanation for the difference between this normal response to eating and the anorexic's response may lie in the fact that eating…or its consequences…can be **very aversive** to people who have been starved. Thus, when someone who has been on a highly restricted diet is faced with a meal they become nauseous, which leads them to avoid the foods that they had eaten. Over time, **conditioned aversions** develop to just about any food…and in the absence of significant positive incentive to eat, anorexics simply stop eating.
- this hypothesis suggests that the best way to treat patients suffering from anorexia nervosa is to limit them to small meals…or infusions of nutrients…until they recover enough to avoid the aversive consequences of eating a meal.

Suggested Websites for Lecture 12b:

Recognizing and Treating Eating Disorders: *http://www.aabainc.org/home.html*
> The home page for the American Anorexia and Bulimia Association.

The Psychobiology of Feeding: *http://www.sciam.com/explorations/1998/030298eating/index.html*
> From Scientific American, an article examining the neural bases of feeding, satiety, and eating disorders. See also:

> *http://www.sciam.com/0896issue/0896gibbs.html*

Eating and Aging: *http://www.sciam.com/specialissues/0600aging/0600taubes.html*
> Also from Scientific American, an interesting article on the link between eating and aging.

**IM-AT-A-GLANCE: Chapter 13. Hormones and Sex:
What's Wrong With the MAMAWAWA?**

Detailed Outline	Print Supplements	Media Supplements	Professor's Notes
Chapter 13. Hormones & Sex: What's The Matter With the MAMAWAWA? pp. 324-349 13.1 The Neuroendocrine System 13.2 Hormones & Sexual Development 13.3 Three Cases of Exceptional Sexual Development 13.4 Effects of Gonadal Hormones on Adults 13.5 The Hypothalamus and Sexual Behavior 13.6 Sexual Orientation, Hormones and the Brain	**Instructor's Manual for** *BIOPSYCHOLOGY,* *Lecture 13a and Lecture 13b* **Test Bank for** *BIOPSYCHOLOGY,* *Chapter 13* **Study Guide for** *BIOPSYCHOLOGY,* *Chapter 13* **Transparencies for Physiological Psychology:** *VIII. Reproductive Behavior*	*Beyond the Brain & Behavior CD for* **BIOPSYCHOLOGY:** *Practice Tests for Chapter 13* *Hard Copy for Chapter 13* *Electronic Flashcards for Chapter 13* **Digital Image Archive, PowerPoint Presentation and Bitmap Images for** *BIOPSYCHOLOGY:* *Chapter 11*	

Lecture 13a

HORMONES AND SEXUAL DEVELOPMENT

Outline

1. The Neuroendocrine System
    a. Glands and Hormones
    b. Gonads
    c. Sex Steroids
    d. Pituitary Gland and the Hypothalamus

2. Hormones and Sexual Development
    a. Fetal Hormones and the Development of Reproductive Organs
    b. Internal Reproductive Ducts
    c. External Reproductive Organs
    d. Brain Development
    e. Behavioral Development
    f. Pubertal

Lecture Notes

-   **hormones** are chemicals released by **endocrine glands** that influence sex in 2 ways: they influence the development of the anatomical, physiological and behavioral characteristics that distinguish males and females, and they activate reproductive behaviors of sexually mature adults
-   when thinking about hormones and sexual behavior, avoid the **MAMAWAWA** assumption

1. **The Neuroendocrine System** (see Fig. 13.1 – Fig. 13.5 in *BIOPSYCHOLOGY;* use *Digital Image Archive Figure CH11F01.BMP - CH11F05.BMP)*

a. Glands & Hormones

-   **exocrine glands** release their chemicals into ducts; **endocrine glands** release hormones directly into the circulatory system
-   there are **3 kinds of hormones: amino acid derivatives; pept**ides and **proteins**; and **steroids.**
-   steroid hormones play the major role in sexual development and behavior
-   like other hormones, steroids can act at **receptors** in cell membranes; unlike other hormones, however, steroids are **small** and **fat soluble** and this allows them to cross the neural membrane to bind to receptors in the cytoplasm or the nucleus

b. Gonads

-   the **gonads** (the **testes** and the **ovaries**) are central to any discussion of hormones and sex
-   they produce **sperm cells** and **ova**
-   at conception, a sperm and ova combine to form a **zygote,** which then contains all of the genetic information needed for the development of a complete adult organism
-   the **sex chromosomes** contain the genetic programs that direct sexual development; female cells contain two large **X chromosomes;** male cells contain one X chromosome and a small **Y chromosome**

c. Sex Steroids

-   the gonads also produce and release the same sex hormones: **androgens, estrogens,** and **progestins**
-   **testosterone** is the most common androgen; **estradiol** is the most common estrogen.

- the **adrenal cortex** also releases all of the sex steroids

d. **Pituitary Gland and the Hypothalamus**

- the pituitary gland is often referred to as the **"master gland"** because it releases a variety of hormones, called **tropic hormones,** which travel through the blood to other glands and stimulate them to release hormones which have diverse, long-lasting effects
- the pituitary is in fact two glands: the **anterior pituitary** and the **posterior pituitary,** which dangle together from the pituitary stalk, which is attached to the **hypothalamus**
- strictly speaking, the anterior pituitary that is the master gland; only it releases tropic hormones
- a major difference between men and women is that **gonadotropin release** from the anterior pituitary **cycles** approximately every 28 days in women, but its release varies little from day to day in men; the release pattern for both sexes is **pulsatile**; attempts to understand this male-female difference led to an important discovery
- first, it was assumed that male and female pituitaries are fundamentally different (**steady vs. cyclic**), but female pituitaries implanted in males became "steady pituitaries", and male pituitaries implanted in females became "cyclic pituitaries"; this suggested that the pattern of anterior pituitary release was being controlled by another organ; it suggested that **"the master gland had its own master"**
- attention turned to the **hypothalamus**, the neural structure to which the pituitary is connected; it was soon discovered that the hypothalamus controls the pituitary in two different ways: one way for the posterior pituitary and one for the anterior pituitary
- axons of neurons in the **paraventricular** and **supraoptic** nuclei of the hypothalamus terminate in the posterior pituitary
- **vasopressin** and **oxytocin** are synthesized in the cell bodies of these neurons, they are transported down their axons, and they are released from the posterior pituitary into general circulation; vasopressin facilitates **reabsorption of water** by the kidneys; oxytocin stimulates **contractions of the uterus** and **ejection of milk** in women
- the release of tropic hormones from the anterior pituitary is controlled by other hormones called **releasing hormones**; they are released by the hypothalamus into the **hypothalamopituitary portal system**, which carries them to the anterior pituitary; gonadotropin-releasing hormone stimulates the release of the anterior pituitary's two **gonadotropins**: **follicle stimulating hormone** and **luteinizing hormone**
- hormone release is regulated by the **nervous system,** which mediates the effects of experience on hormone release; by **feedback** of the hormones themselves onto receptors in the same structures responsible for their release (this system maintains blood levels of the hormones); and by **nonhormonal chemicals** such as glucose, calcium and sodium (this system regulates the levels of these chemicals).

2. *Hormones and Sexual Development* (see Fig. 13.6 – Fig. 13.9 in *BIOPSYCHOLOGY;* use *Digital Image Archive Figure CH11F02.BMP, CH11F03.BMP, CH11F04.BMP, CH11F05.BMP)*

a. **Fetal Hormones and the Development of Reproductive Organs**

- the differentiation of male and female gonads occurs about 6 weeks after fertilization, at this time males and females have identical **primordial gonads,** each with two parts: a **medulla** and a **cortex**
- in males, the Y chromosome triggers the manufacture of a protein called **H-Y antigen,** which causes the medulla (core) of the primordial gonads to develop into testes
- if no H-Y antigen is present (as in normal genetic females), the cortex of the primordial gonads naturally develops into ovaries
- accordingly, genetic female fetuses injected with H-Y antigen develop testes, and genetic male fetuses injected with a drug that blocks H-Y antigen develop ovaries

b. **Internal Reproductive Ducts**

- 6 weeks after fertilization each fetus has two sets of undeveloped internal reproductive ducts, one male and one female; the undeveloped male system is called the **Wolffian system**; the undeveloped female system is called the **Müllerian System**
- in normal genetic males, the testes release androgens in the third month and this causes the Wolffian system to develop; the testes also release **Müllerian-inhibiting substance**, which causes the Müllerian system to degenerate and the testes to descend into the scrotum; all fetuses exposed to androgen in the third month, whether genetic male or female, develop male ducts
- any fetus not exposed to androgens in the third month after conception (e.g., a normal genetic female, an ovariectomized genetic female, or an orchidectomized genetic male) will develop female reproductive ducts
- **ovariectomy** refers specifically to removal of the ovaries; **orchidectomy** refers specifically to removal of the testes; **castration** and **gonadectomy** refer generally to removal of gonads

c. **External Reproductive Organs**

- every normal human fetus begins with the same **bipotential precursor** of external reproductive organs
- there are 4 parts to the bipotential precursor: the **glans,** the **urethral folds,** the **lateral bodies,** and the **labioscrotal swellings.**
- in males, the glans become the **head of the penis;** the urethral folds simply fuse; the lateral bodies form the **shaft** of the penis; and the labioscrotal folds become the **scrotum**
- in females, the glans become the **clitoris;** the urethral folds become the **labia minora**; the lateral bodies form the **hood** of the clitoris; and the labioscrotal folds become the **labia majora**
- like the internal reproductive organs, testosterone release at the right time in development causes this bipotential precursor to develop into male external genitals; in the absence of testosterone it develops into female external genitals

d. **Brain Development**

- there is growing evidence of differences between men and women in terms of **overall brain size**, the size of **specific structures** in the brain, and in **patterns of brain activity**
- the functional significance of these differences is unclear
- similar to the differentiation of other body organs, sexual differences in the brain appear to depend on exposure to high levels of androgens at **developmentally crucial times**
- rats are often used to study of the sexual differentiation of the brain because when they are born the period during which the development of the brain is maximally influenced by hormones is just beginning
- most early research on brain differentiation focused on the differentiation of the hypothalamus-controlled pattern of **gonadotropin release** into the steady male pattern or the female cyclic pattern
- consistent with what you have already learned about reproductive-system development, rats exposed to androgens in the perinatal period (e.g., intact genetic male rats, intact genetic female rats injected with androgen, ovariectomized female rats injected with androgen) develop the steady, male pattern of gonadotropin release
- in contrast, rats not exposed to androgen in the perinatal period (e.g., intact genetic female rats, ovariectomized genetic female rats, orchidectomized genetic male rats) develop the cyclic, female pattern of gonadotropin release
- there is evidence to support the idea that in order to masculinize the brain **testosterone** must be converted to **estradiol**--a process called **aromatization**
- the **aromatization hypothesis** is that testosterone released during the perinatal period enters the brain and is aromatized to estradiol and that it is actually estradiol that masculinizes the brain
- four lines of evidence support this theory: (1) the **enzyme** necessary for aromatization is present in the neonates; (2) **neonatal injections** of estradiol masculinize the brain, (3) **dihydrotestosterone**, a nonaromatizable androgen, does not masculinize the brain, and (4) agents that **block aromatization** block the masculinizing effects of neonatal testosterone injections

e. Behavioral Development

- considerable attention has been paid to the role of hormones on the development of sexual behavior
- Phoenix and colleagues (1955) demonstrated that perinatal injections of testosterone **masculinizes** and **defeminizes** a genetic female's copulatory behaviors; as adults, such females display male-like mounting behaviors when injected with testosterone and they display less **lordosis** when injected with progesterone and estradiol
- alternatively, male rats that are not exposed to testosterone early in development are **feminized** and **demasculinized**
- in addition, perinatal testosterone alters the **proceptive behaviors** displayed by rats; there is less hopping, darting and ear wiggling by receptive female rats; female rats tend to be more aggressive when they mature; and their maternal behaviors are also altered

f. Puberty

- **puberty** marks the transition between childhood and adulthood, the start of the adolescent growth spurt, and the development of **secondary sex characteristics**
- at the beginning of puberty, there is a surge in the release of **growth hormone** and of both the **gonadotropic** and **adrenocorticotropic hormones** from the anterior pituitary; the latter hormones elicit the release of hormones from the gonads and adrenal cortex which initiate the maturation of the genitals and the development of the secondary sex characteristics
- in **males** the surge in **gonadotropic hormones** increases the release of **androgens** from the testes
- this masculinizes the body; there is muscle development, body hair and pubic hair growth, lowering of the voice, the development of fertility, growth of sex organs, etc.
- in **females** the pubertal surge of gonadotropin release stimulates the release of estrogens from the ovaries
- this partially feminizes the body; estrogens stimulate breast growth, hip growth, onset of the menstrual cycle, fertility, etc.

Suggested Websites for Lecture 13a:

Gender and Brain: *http://www.science.ca/scientists/scientistprofile.php?pID=10*
> A biography of sorts of Doreen Kimura, highlighting her work on sex differences in brain function.

Behavioral Neuroendocrinology: *http://www.sbne.org/*
> Homepage for the Behavioral Neuroendocrinology Society and its journal, Hormones and Behavior.

Sex Differences and the Brain: *http://www.sciencedaily.com/releases/1999/05/990518072823.htm*
> From the Science Daily webnews site, reviews recent work looking at functional correlates of sex differences and cognitive function.

Lecture 13b

THE EFFECTS OF SEX HORMONES IN
PUBERTY AND ADULTHOOD

Outline

1. Exceptional Cases of Human Sexual Development
   a. Androgenic Insensitivity Syndrome
   b. Androgenital Syndrome
   c. Ablation Penis

2. Effects of Gonadal Hormones in Adulthood
   a. Males
   b. Females
   c. Anabolic Steroid Use

3. The Hypothalamus and Sexual Behavior

4. Sexual Orientation, Hormones and the Brain

Lecture Notes

1. **Exceptional Cases of Human Sexual Development**

   a. **Androgenic Insensitivity Syndrome**

   - there are otherwise normal genetic males who suffer from the **androgen insensitivity syndrome**; they have normal levels of androgen but their bodies lack the receptors to not respond to it
   - genetic males with androgen insensitivity frequently come to the attention of a physician when they become concerned about their inability to get pregnant; they are ostensibly happily married women
   - a physical examination reveals: (1) sparse **pubic** and **axillary hair,** (2) they do not **menstruate,** (3) they have **shallow vaginas,** (4) they have **internal testes** and undeveloped male internal reproductive ducts, and (5) their cells are all of the normal male **XY chromosome** type
   - during development, individuals with Androgenic Insensitivity Syndrome develop along preprogrammed female lines, without the overriding effects of androgens
   - Money and Earhardt (1972) found that the childhood behavior of these patients were those one would expect of a female; in spite of their genetic maleness, they looked like females, were raised like females…and they acted like females

   b. **Androgenital Syndrome**

   - results from a deficiency in the release of **cortisol** from the adrenal cortex; this causes adrenal hyperactivity and excessive release of adrenal androgens
   - males are generally unaffected; females are often born with an **enlarged clitoris** and a **partially fused labia**, though the **internal reproductive organs** are usually normal
   - this disorder is usually detected at birth; administration of cortisol reduces the levels of the adrenal androgens
   - females who receive early treatment still display a high degree of **tomboyishness** and little interest in maternity when they are teenagers; however, their behavior is still well within the normal range
   - in adulthood, females who receive early treatment show **normal sexual preferences**

    c. **Ablatio Penis**

- as the name implies, this is a condition produced when the **penis is removed**
- in the most famous case, a baby's penis was accidentally destroyed during a circumcision; the child was castrated, an **artificial vagina** was created, and estrogen was administered to **feminize** the boy
- as this case was originally reported by Money (1975), the boy developed into a "normal" female...supporting the idea that **"Nurture can overcome Nature."**
- long-term follow-ups tell a different story; the child acted in a masculine way, he suspected he was a boy beginning in the second grade, and he moved and talked in a masculine manner
- by age 14 the boy had decided to be a male...and was only then told of his early history. He requested androgen treatments; had a **mastectomy** and **phaloplasty** (removal of breasts and surgical creation of a penis); married at 25 and became strictly **heterosexual**...he could ejaculate and experience orgasm, though the castration left him permanently sterile.

2. **Effects of Gonadal Hormones in Adulthood** (see Fig. 13.10 – Fig. 13.11 in *BIOPSYCHOLOGY*)

- hormones not only influence the **development** of the body and brain along male or female lines, they play a role in **activating** the sexual behavior of men and women

    a. **Males**

- the role of androgens in activating the sexual behavior of adult males is apparent following **orchidectomy**
- in about half the cases, there is a complete loss of ability to achieve **an erection** and of **sexual motivation** within a week or two of the operation; however, in other cases, the decline is less complete and/or more gradual; the reason for this **variability** is not understood
- castrated men also exhibit a variety of **physical changes**, e.g., reduction of body hair, deposition of fat on hips and chest, softening of the skin, a marked reduction of strength
- **testosterone replacement injections** restore sexual motivation, sexual potency, and remasculinize the bodies of orchidectomized males; but they remain **sterile**
- the fact that testosterone injections restore the sexuality of orchidectomized males has led to the view that the **sexual motivation and performance** of a male is determined by his level of **testosterone,** and thus that sexual motivation and performance can be increased in healthy intact males by testosterone injections
- **this is NOT the case;** in healthy intact males there is no correlation between testosterone levels and sexuality, and substantial increases (e.g., by injection) or decreases (e.g., by **hemiorchidectomy**) in testosterone levels have no effect on sexual motivation or performance

    b. **Females**

- in female rodents, the 4 or 5 day menstrual cycle is correlated with a cycle of sexual receptivity (i.e., with an **estrous cycle**)
- in the day or two prior to ovulation, there is a gradual increase in estrogens, and a sudden surge in progesterone just as the mature egg is being released from its follicle
- during the next 12 to 18 hours the female is said to be in **estrus**: that is, she is **fertile, receptive, proceptive,** and **sexually attractive** to male rats
- **ovariectomy** abolishes the estrous cycle in rodents; but ovariectomized female rodents can be readily brought into estrus by an injection of estradiol followed a day and a half later by an injection of progesterone
- **human females are different;** there is no clear-cut cycle of sexual receptivity associated with the menstrual cycle; ovariectomy eliminates vaginal lubrication, the menstrual cycle, and fertility, but it has no effect on **sexual motivation**
- the sexual motivation of human females appears to be maintained by **androgens;** sexual motivation is lost following **ovariectomy** plus **adrenalectomy,** but is reinstated by replacement androgen injections, and sexual motivation appears to correlate with levels of testosterone but not estrogen

c. Anabolic Steroid Use

- testosterone has **anabolic** (growth promoting) effects, but it is not a particularly effective anabolic agent because it is quickly broken down in the body
- chemists have synthesized similar chemicals belonging to the same class (steroids) that are not broken down so quickly; these are the so-called **anabolic steroids**; there is currently an epidemic of anabolic steroid abuse among athletes
- although the experimental evidence may be considered ambiguous, there is considerable evidence (experimental and anecdotal) evidence that anabolic steroids can increase the **muscularity, strength,** and **performance** of both male and female athletes
- however, there are a number of devastating side-effects: **testicular atrophy** and **gynecomastia** (breast growth) have been reported in **men; amenorrhea**, sterility, **hirsutism** (excessive growth of body hair), growth of the clitoris, masculine body shape, baldness, and deepening of the voice have been reported in **women**
- in both men and women, there have been reports of muscle pain, muscle spasms, excessive water retention, acne, nausea, vomiting, bleeding of the tongue, fits of anger, aggression, or depression, and premature death

3. **The Hypothalamus and Sexual Behavior** (see Fig. 13.1 – Fig. 13.5 in *BIOPSYCHOLOGY;* use *Digital Image Archive,* **Figure CH11F02.BMP,** *CH11F13.BMP* and CH11F15.BMP)

- the role of the hypothalamus in the control of the pituitary gland led to an examination of sex differences in the hypothalamus
- notably, the **sexually dimorphic nucleus** in the **medial preoptic area** in rats was found to be several times larger in males than in females
- at birth, the sexually dimorphic nucleus is the same size in both sexes; however, within the first few days postnatal this area grows rapidly in males but not females. This growth is stimulated by estradiol, aromatized from testosterone; castration at day-1 postnatal reduces the size of the medial preoptic in adult rats.
- the size of the sexually dimorphic nucleus has been correlated with **testosterone levels** and some aspects of **sexual behavior.** However, bilateral lesions of the nucleus have only slight effects on male rat sexual behavior and its function remains unclear.
- in males, the medial preoptic area plays a key role in sexual behavior; lesions abolish sexual behavior in all areas studied, and stimulation in the area elicits copulatory behavior
- interestingly, lesions to the medial preoptic area do not diminish the desire for sexual behavior, just copulatory behavior
- the medial preoptic area seems to influence copulatory behavior via the **lateral tegmental fields;** lesions here also eliminate copulatory behavior in rodents
- in female rats, the **ventromedial nucleus** of the thalamus contains circuits critical to sexual behavior; stimulation elicits these behaviors, and lesions there reduce it.
- the ventromedial thalamic nucleus is critical to the **onset of estrus** in female rats, as microinjections of estrogen and progesterone there will bring on estrus.
- the ventromedial thalamic nucleus appears to act via a projection to the **periaqueductal gray**.

4. **Sexual Orientation, Hormones and the Brain**

- many humans are not **heterosexual**; they are sexually attracted to members of the same bodily sex (**homosexual**), or to members of both bodily sexes (**bisexual**)
- sexual orientation appears to have a **genetic basis;** for example, monozygotic twins of homosexuals have a concordance rate of about 50%
- there are no differences in circulating sex hormones between homosexuals and heterosexuals
- in animals, perinatal castration of males or testosterone treatment of females induces **same-sex preferences**

- the relevance of these data to humans are **unclear;** the experiments necessary to test the idea that early hormone exposure has a role in sexual orientation cannot be ethically performed on humans, and homosexuality and bisexuality are difficult to model in nonhumans
- however, Ehrhardt and her colleagues found the prenatal exposure to **diethylstilbestrol,** a synthetic estrogen, increased females attraction to other women but did not seem to significantly alter their sexual orientation
- sexual attraction emerges at around the **age of 10** and appears to be due to **adrenal androgens**
- LeVay (1991) found that the **third interstitial nucleus of the hypothalamus** is more than twice as large in heterosexual males than it is in heterosexual females and homosexual males
- however, it is not clear whether this difference was a cause or a product of the homosexual preferences of his subjects

Suggested Websites for Lecture 13b:

Androgen Insensitivity: *http://www.medhelp.org/www/ais/*
A page devoted to androgen insensitivity syndrome.

Sex, Flies, and Genes: *http://www.sciam.com/0697issue/0697scicit4.html*
Evidence that sexual behavior is under a certain degree of genetic control...at least in fruit flies! From the Scientific American's *Science and the Citizen* page.

How the Brain Organizes Sexual Behavior: *http://www.epub.org.br/cm/n03/mente/sexo_i.htm*
Another good link to the Brain and Mind e-magazine from the State University of Campinas, Brazil; a review of the physiology of coitus and the influence that the brain has on sexual preference and its control of sexual behavior.

IM-AT-A-GLANCE: Chapter 14. Sleep, Dreaming and Circadian Rhythms: How Much Do You Need to Sleep?

Detailed Outline	Print Supplements	Media Supplements	Professor's Notes
Chapter 14. Sleep, Dreaming and Circadian Rhythms: How Much Do You Need to Sleep? pp. 350-379 14.1 The Physiological and Behavioral Events of Sleep 14.2 REM Sleep & Dreaming 14.3 Why Do We Sleep, and Why Do We Sleep When We Do? 14.4 Comparative Analysis of Sleep 14.5 Circadian Sleep Cycles 14.6 Effects of Sleep Deprivation 14.7 Neural Mechanisms of Sleep 14.8 The Circadian Clock: Neural and Molecular Mechanisms 14.9 Drugs That Affect Sleep 14.10 Sleep Disorders 14.11 The Effects of Long-Term Sleep Reduction	**Instructor's Manual for** *BIOPSYCHOLOGY,* *Lecture 14a and Lecture 14b* **Test Bank for** *BIOPSYCHOLOGY,* *Chapter 14* **Study Guide for** *BIOPSYCHOLOGY,* *Chapter 14* **Transparencies for Physiological Psychology:** *IX. Sleep*	**Beyond the Brain & Behavior CD for** *BIOPSYCHOLOGY:* *Good Morning module* *Practice Tests for Chapter 14* *Hard Copy for Chapter 14* *Electronic Flashcards for Chapter 14* **Digital Image Archive, PowerPoint Presentation and Bitmap Images for** *BIOPSYCHOLOGY:* *Chapter 12* *BIOLOGICAL PSYCHOLOGY VIDEO:* *Segment 10. Dreams*	

Lecture 14a

THE PHYSIOLOGICAL AND BEHAVIORAL CORRELATES
OF SLEEP AND DREAMING

Outline

1.   Three Psychophysiological Measures of Sleep

2.   The Five Stages of Sleep EEG

3.   REM Sleep and Dreaming

4.   Why Sleep?
     a.   Recuperation Theories
     b.   Circadian Theories

5. Comparative Analysis of Sleep

6. Circadian Sleep Cycles

7. Effects of Sleep Reduction
     a.   Total Sleep Deprivation
     b.   REM Deprivation

Lecture Notes

1.   **Three Psychophysiological Measures of Sleep** (see Fig. 14.1 *BIOPSYCHOLOGY)*

     -   in the 1930s, it was discovered that although **EEG** waves are generally high-voltage and slow during sleep, there are periods during sleep when they are similar to the low-voltage fast waves of wakefulness
     -   in 1953, Aserinsky and Kleitman discovered that **rapid eye movements (REMs)** occurred under the eyelids of sleeping subjects during the periods of low-voltage fast EEG activity
     -   in 1962, Berger and Oswald found that there was a dramatic decline of **EMG (electromyogram)** activity in the muscles of the body core during these same sleep periods
     -   since these three discoveries, **EEG, EOG (electrooculogram),** and **EMG** have been monitored in most sleep experiments

2.   **The Four Stages of Sleep EEG** (see Fig. 14.2 and Fig. 14.3 in *BIOPSYCHOLOGY;* use *Digital Image Archive Figure CH12F02.BMP* and *CH12F02.BMP)*

     -   just before a subject falls asleep, the EEG is typically punctuated by bursts of **alpha waves** (large-amplitude, regular, 8-to-12-Hz waves indicative of relaxed wakefulness)
     -   when the subject falls asleep, the EEG progresses in sequence through initial stage 1, stage 2, stage 3, and stage 4
     -   **initial stage 1 sleep EEG** is low-voltage, fast activity similar to, but slightly slower than, that of wakefulness
     -   **stage 2 sleep EEG** is of higher voltage and slower than stage 1; its most obvious characteristics are **K complexes** (a single large negative wave followed by a single large positive wave) and **sleep spindles** (1-to-2-second waxing-and-waning bursts of 12-to-15-Hz waves)
     -   **stage 3 sleep EEG** is defined by the occasional presence of **delta waves**, the largest and slowest EEG waves (1 to 2 per second)
     -   **stage 4 sleep EEG** is defined by a predominance of delta waves

- once the sleeping subject has gone through initial stage 1 to stage 4, he or she goes back through the stages to stage 1 EEG
- but when the subject returns to stage 1 EEG, it is referred to as **emergent stage 1 EEG** because it emerges from the other stages. The rest of the night is spent going between emergent stage 1 through to stage 4 sleep, and then back again.
- it is important to distinguish between initial stage 1 EEG and emergent stage 1 EEG because only emergent stage 1 EEG is associated with **REMs** and low levels of muscle tonus in core muscles
- the stage during which emergent stage 1 occurs is often called **REM sleep** or **paradoxical sleep** (it was initially considered a paradox that subjects slept while their EEGs suggested that they were awake); stages 2, 3, and 4 together are often referred to as **slow-wave sleep**; stages 3 and 4 together are often referred to as **delta sleep**
- the progression of EEG stages changes during a typical night's sleep: each cycle is about **90 minutes long;** as the night progresses less time is spent in stages 3 and 4 and more is spent in REM sleep; and there are brief periods of wakefulness, which are normally forgotten in the morning

3. **REM Sleep and Dreaming** (use *Biological Psychology* video, *Segment 10. Dreams)*

- the discovery of REMs in 1953 by Kleitman and his colleagues led to the obvious hypothesis that **REM-sleep periods were periods of dreaming;** this hypothesis was confirmed by waking subjects up during various stages of sleep and asking them if they had been dreaming; about 80% of awakenings from REM sleep led to dream reports, and only 7% of awakenings from nonREM-sleep stages led to dream reports
- in the years since this discovery, a number of common beliefs about dreaming have been objectively tested by using EEG, EMG, and EOG indices of dreaming:

   (1) Are **external stimuli** incorporated into dream sequences? (Yes, dripping water onto subjects was in 14 out of 33 dream cases)
   (2) Do dreams run on **"real time"**? (Yes, subjects awakened 5 or 15 minutes after the beginning of a dream could guess the correct interval on the basis of the contents of their dreams)
   (3) Does **everybody** dream? (Yes, even people who claimed that they did not dream had normal amounts of REM, and they reported dreams if they were awakened during REM-- although less frequently);
   (4) Are **penile erections** indicative of dreams with sexual content? (No, penile and clitoral tumescence occurs during all dreams, regardless of sexual content);
   (5) Are **somnambulism** and **sleep talking** the acting out of dreams? (No, they usually occur during stage 4);

- The **Freudian theory of dreams,** that dreams represent unacceptable (often sexual) wishes, was based on science and beliefs of the 1890's and has **no support** from today's science base
- Hobson's has proposed an **activation-synthesis theory** of dreaming, based upon the idea that the information passed on to the cortex during REM is random, and dreams are the cortex's effort to make sense of these **random signals**
- A few people have **lucid dreams** in which the dreamer knows that they are dreaming and can change the course of their dreams; lucid dreams are usually **positive experiences**

4. **Why Sleep?**

- two types of theories have developed to account for why we sleep: **recuperation theories** and **circadian theories**

   a. **Recuperation Theories**

   - the essence of various **recuperation theories** of sleep is that being awake disrupts **homeostasis** in some way and that sleep is required to **restore** it
   - this is the way that most people think about sleep

     b.   Circadian Theories

- according to the **circadian theory** of sleep, sleep is not a response to an internal imbalance; sleep is an **adaptive response** that evolved to **conserve energy** and to **protect organisms** from mishap and predation; the urge to sleep evolved to be greatest during the night for animals who do not see well in dim illumination
- the circadian theory of sleep considers sleep to be like sexual behavior; it is adaptive and there is a strong drive to engage in it, but its purpose is not to correct an inner deficiency

- three lines of research have a direct bearing on whether sleep is fundamentally recuperative or circadian: 1) the comparative study of sleep; 2) study of circadian sleep cycles; and 3) the study of the effects of sleep reduction

5. **Comparative Analyses of Sleep** (see Fig. 14.4 and Table 14.1 in *BIOPSYCHOLOGY*)

- all **mammals** and **bird** sleep in a fashion similar to humans; **fish, reptiles, amphibians** and **insects** also go through periods of inactivity similar to sleep
- the fact that **all animals sleep** suggests that sleep in not uniquely human, but has evolved for some sort of important physiologic reason
- differences in sleep duration suggest that it is into needed in large amounts; many animals sleep only **2-3 hr** per night
- sleep duration seems to be correlated with how **vulnerable** a species is when it sleeps; predators tend to sleep longer, whereas prey species sleep for shorter periods of time

6. **Circadian Sleep-Wake Cycles** (see Fig. 14.5 *BIOPSYCHOLOGY;* use *Digital Image Archive Figure CH12F05.BMP)*

- almost every physiological function in surface-dwelling animals displays some kind of circadian rhythmicity; the sleep-wake cycle is the most obvious
- the light-dark cycle is an important factor in the timing of most **circadian rhythms**; environmental cues (such as the light-dark cycle) that **entrain** circadian rhythms are called **zeitgebers**
- however, sleep-wake cycles still cycle regularly in a constant environment; regular biological cycles in constant environments are called **free-running cycles**; the duration of a free-running cycle is its **free-running period**
- even animals raised from birth in unchanging laboratory environments display highly regular free-running cycles; circadian cycles thus **do not appear to be learned**
- sometimes sleep-wake cycles and body temperature cycles can break away from one another so that they are out of phase: this is called **internal desynchronization,** and suggests that there is more than one circadian timing mechanism in the brain
- the fact that such regularity is precisely maintained despite large day-to-day variations in physical and mental activity is strong support for **circadian theories** of sleep
- several studies have found a **negative correlation** between the length of a period of wakefulness and the length of the following period of sleep, even under free-running conditions; this is the opposite of what the recuperation theory would predict
- it seems that we are programmed to go to sleep every 24 hours or so; if we stay awake longer than usual during a particular 24-hour cycle, there is less time left for sleep in that cycle
- alternating **shift work** and **jet lag** are situations where zeitgebers are **phase advanced** (moving to an earlier shift or flying east) or **phase delayed** (moving to a later shift or flying west); people must adjust their natural sleep-wake cycles or endure problems such as sleep disturbances, fatigue, and performance decrements; phase advances are more difficult adjustments than are phase delays

7. **Effects of Sleep Deprivation** (see Fig. 14.7 and Fig. 14.8 in *BIOPSYCHOLOGY;* use *Digital Image Archive Figure CH12F06.BMP)*

a. Total Sleep Deprivation

- the third line of research that has a direct bearing on the question of whether sleep is fundamentally circadian or recuperative is research on **sleep reduction**
- the recuperation theory predicts: 1) that long periods of wakefulness will result in **debilitating physiological deficits;** 2) that these deficits will grow **steadily worse** as the sleep deprivation continue; and 3) that after the sleep deprivation has ended, much of the lost sleep will be **regained**
- there are many studies in which subjects have been totally deprived of sleep for several days; these studies have not confirmed the predictions of the recuperation theory
- **no marked physiological disturbances** other than increased sleepiness have been discovered in sleep-deprived subjects;
- sleep deprived subjects often display **mood disturbances** and problems **maintaining vigilance**
- after 2-3 days of sleep deprivation, subjects experience **microsleeps** (2-or-3-second periods during which subjects remain sitting or standing but their **eyelids droop** and they are **unresponsive** to external stimuli)
- sleep deprivation in lab animals has suggested that sleep plays a **critical role** to the well-being of an organism, as several days of total sleep deprivation has led to subject mortality. However, these data should be **interpreted with caution** as the sleep-deprivation paradigms used in these studies appeared to **severely stress** the animals involved.

b. REM-Sleep Deprivation

- because REM sleep is associated with dreaming, there has been much interest in the effects of the selective deprivation of REM sleep
- there are two major effects of REM sleep deprivation:
  - i) REM deprivation is enforced by waking subjects up each time that REMs begin to occur; as a period of REM deprivation progresses, subjects must be awakened more and more frequently to prevent them from having periods of REM sleep; and
  - ii) after REM deprivation is curtailed, **REM rebound** is often seen; subjects get more than their normal amount of REM sleep for the next two or three nights
- one of the main challenges for anyone suggesting that REM sleep is critical to normal functioning must explain why **tricyclic antidepressants,** which block REM sleep at common therapeutic doses, produce but patients who have taken them regularly for years have experienced no adverse psychological side effects that can be attributed to REM deprivation

Suggested Websites for Lecture 14a:

Sleep Stages: *http://www.sleepdisorderchannel.net/stages/*
A comprehensive review of sleep stages from the SleepChannel website.

Dr. Dement: *http://www.sleepquest.com/d_column.html*
The opinions and commentary of Dr. Daniel Dement, a pioneer in sleep research; part of the Sleep Well website.

Learning & Dreaming: *http://www.sciencefriday.com/pages/2001/Feb/hour2_020901.html*
From National Public Radio, a RealTime audio interview with Dr. Robert Stickgold and Dr. Matt Wilson on the role of dreaming in learning and memory.

Biorhythms: *http://www.srbr.org/*
Site maintained by the Society for Research on Biological Rhythms.

Lecture 14b

WHY DO WE SLEEP?

Outline

1. Neural Mechanisms of Sleep

2. The Circadian Clock
   a. The Suprachiasmatic Nucleus
   b. Mechanisms of Entrainment

3. Drugs That Affect Sleep
   a. Hypnotic Drugs
   b. Antihypnotic Drugs
   c. Melatonin

4. Sleep Disorders
   a. Insomnia
   b. Hypersomnia
   c. REM-related sleep disorders

5. Effects of Long-Term Sleep Reduction

Lecture Notes

1. **Neural Mechanisms of Sleep** (see Fig. 14.9 - Fig. 14.12 in *BIOPSYCHOLOGY;* use *Digital Image Archive Figure CH12F11.BMP - CH12F14.BMP)*

   - Bremer proposed the first major theory of sleep physiology; he proposed that a **passive theory of sleep** in which sleep occurs because of a reduction of sensory input to the forebrain; in support of this idea, he found that cutting the brainstem between the **superior** and **inferior colliculi** (a **cerveau isolé** preparation) produced a state of almost continuous slow-wave sleep
   - this idea was replaced by an **active theory of sleep** based around the idea of a **reticular activating system.** Three findings contributed to this new theory:

      i) cutting the brainstem at the caudal end (and **encephalé isolé** preparation) did not affect sleep, although such surgery damaged most of the same sensory pathways as the cerveau isolé preparation;
      ii) the **cerveau isolé** preparation only impaired sleep when it transected the reticular activating system core of the brainstem, and
      iii) electrical stimulation of the reticular activating system in sleeping cats awakened them

   - the research generated by this hypothesis led to the discovery that **sleep is NOT a passive process;** the brain is still very active, and in some areas neurons are more active during sleep than they are during waking hours.
   - in addition, some areas of the brainstem actually **promote sleep** when they are stimulated; thus, sleep is not due to a decrease in all brain activity
   - finally, **REM sleep** and **slow-wave sleep** can be **dissociated**

- several brain regions have been implicated in regulation of sleep; these include:

    i) the **raphe nuclei,** a thin cluster of **serotonin-releasing nuclei** that lie along the midline of the caudal reticular formation; lesions here produce **insomnia**

    ii) the **basal forebrain,** including the **anterior hypothalamus;** lesions here reduce sleep duration

    iii) the **caudal reticular formation REM-sleep circuits;** various sites in the brainstem control different aspects of REM sleep

2. The Circadian Clock (see Fig. 14.13 in *BIOPSYCHOLOGY;* use *Digital Image Archive, Figure CH12F16.BMP)*

a. The Suprachiasmatic Nucleus

- the fact that animals can maintain circadian cycles in the absence of external cues suggests that there is an internal timing mechanism
- the first clue as to the location of this structure in the brain came when it was discovered that lesions of the **medial hypothalamus,** and more specifically the **suprachiasmatic nuclei (SCN),** disrupts various circadian cycles
- cells in the SCN maintain circadian cycles even when the tissue is **excised** from the rest of the brain; stimulation here **shifts free-running cycles**

b. Mechanisms of Entrainment

- the 24-hr light-dark cycle entrains various circadian cycles via direct axonal connections between the **retina** and the SCN (these are the **retinohypothalamic tracts).** Amazingly, rods and cones do NOT appear to be necessary for this entrainment to occur!
- there are at least **8 circadian genes** that have been identified to date; these have been found in various types of tissue, and they appear to be conserved in a wide variety of organisms (ranging from **bacteria to humans**), suggesting that they appeared early in evolutionary history

3. Drugs That Affect Sleep (see Fig. 14.14 in *BIOPSYCHOLOGY)*

a. Hypnotic Drugs

- **hypnotic drugs** are drugs that increase sleep; the most common hypnotic drugs are the **benzodiazepines** (e.g., Valium)
- they should not be prescribed for long-term sleep problems as they all suffer from the development of **tolerance** to their hypnotic effects; they produce **insomnia** as part of their withdrawal syndrome; they are **addictive;** and they **distort the normal sleep pattern**
- serotonergic agonists like **5-hydroxytryptophan** (the precursor for serotonin) have proven ineffective in the treatment of insomnia

b. Antihypnotic Drugs

- these drugs decrease sleep; the most common antihypnotic drugs are the **stimulants** (e.g., **cocaine**) and **tricyclic antidepressants**
- both types of drugs increase the activity of neurons releasing **catecholamine** (dopamine; norepinephrine) neurotransmitters
- both types of drugs preferentially reduce REM sleep, even at doses that have little effect on total sleep time
- these drugs have many unwanted side-effects; they are **addictive;** they **suppress appetite;** and they may **interfere** with normal sleep patterns

c. Melatonin

- **melatonin** is a hormone synthesized from **serotonin** in the **pineal gland**
- this gland has **inherent timing properties** and is important in some species in the regulation of circadian cycles and **seasonal changes in reproductive behavior**
- the role of the pineal in humans is not clear; though it produces circadian rhythms in melatonin release and is believed to play a role in promoting sleep, **pinealectomy** has little effect on a person's behavior

4. Sleep Disorders

a. Insomnia

- problems with initiating and maintaining sleep
- is often **iatrogenic** (physician-created), due to prescription of hypnotic drugs like Valium
- **sleep apnea** is another common form of insomnia; the patient stops breathing while they sleep, many times each night. Each time, they awake, begin to breathe again, then fall asleep…only to stop breathing again.
- **nocturnal myoclonus** and **restless legs** are two other causes of insomnia
- in one study, people seeking help for insomnia claimed that they slept an average of 4.5 hours per night, but they actually slept about 6.5 hours per night; they were suspected of being **pseudoinsomniacs** until studies found that many such patients were suffering from sleep-disturbing problems such as sleep apnea or nocturnal myoclonus; it seems that undisturbed sleep rather than sleep per se is what we need to feel rested
- **sleep restriction** is an effective treatment for many forms of insomnia; a patient's sleep is greatly restricted, and then slowly increased in duration

b. Hypersomnia

- problems of excessive or inappropriate sleep; sleep promoting conditions are called **soporific**
- the most studied disorder of hypersomnia is **narcolepsy;** narcoleptics tend to fall asleep in totally inappropriate situations (while having conversations, eating, or scuba diving), they usually sleep for 10 or 15 minutes and then awaken
- **cataplexy** is another symptom of narcolepsy; patients lose muscle tone during wakefulness, often falling to the ground as though they were shot
- narcoleptics also often display **sleep paralysis** (inability to move when falling asleep) and **hypnagogic hallucinations** (dreamlike experiences during wakefulness)
- may be due to inappropriate activity in the **nucleus magnocellularis** in the caudal reticular formation; normally neurons here are active only during **REM sleep;** in narcoleptic dogs, these neurons are also active during their narcoleptic attacks
- research in narcoleptic dogs has also revealed a gene that causes the disorder; the gene codes for a receptor that binds a protein called **orexin**

c. REM-Sleep-Related Disorders

- **narcoleptics** go directly into REM sleep rather than going through other sleep stages, thus narcolepsy is often categorized with REM-sleep-related disorders
- occasionally patients will suffer from brain damage that prevents REM sleep; these patients appear to suffer few negative consequences
- some patients experience REM sleep without core muscle atonia; these people are able to act out their dreams; it is believed this is due to damage to the nucleus magnocellularis

5. Effects of Long-Term Sleep Reduction

- two studies have maintained subjects on programs of sleep-reduction
- in general, there appear to be few negative consequences to sleep-reduction
- for example, Friedman and colleagues asked subjects to reduce their sleep in 30-minute steps every few weeks until they felt that they did not want to reduce it further; then they slept at this shortest time for 1 month and at the shortest time plus 30 minutes for 2 months; finally, the subjects' natural sleep time was measured 1 year after they had returned to sleeping for as long as they pleased
- subjects achieved a minimum sleep duration of between 4.5 - 5.5 hours per night there was a major **increase in sleep efficiency** (less time to fall asleep, fewer awakenings, more stage 4 sleep); there were **no deficits** on any of the numerous performance and psychological tests given throughout the experiment; and 1 year after the period of sleep restriction, all subjects were naturally sleeping between 7 and 18 hours less per week
- a particularly powerful method of sleep reduction involves the adoption of a **polyphasic sleep cycle** (sleeping more than once per day); for example, Leonardo da Vinci adopted a pattern of sleeping for 15 min, every 4 hr…for a total of just 1.5 hr per day!

Suggested Websites for Lecture 14b:

Biological and Circadian Rhythms: *http://www.epub.org.br/cm/n04/mente/cloks_i.htm*
From the Brain and Mind site, an overview of the neural structures involved in establishing circadian rhythms; good figures, and links to related sites. See also:

Sleep Deprivation: *http://www.mhsource.com/edu/psytimes/p980301b.html*
A provocative article by Dr. Stanley Cohen, highlighting the possible negative effects of long-term sleep deprivation.

Melatonin and Sleep: *http://www.sciam.com/explorations/040196explorations.html*
From Scientific American, a critical look at the "drug of darkness", the neurohormone and putative sleep aid melatonin.

Sleep Disorders: *http://www.nhlbi.nih.gov/about/ncsdr/index.htm*
The National Center on Sleep Disorders Research, from the National Institutes of Health

IM-AT-A-GLANCE: Chapter 15. Drug Addiction and
The Brain's Reward Circuits: Chemicals That Harm with Pleasure

Detailed Outline	Print Supplements	Media Supplements	Professor's Notes
Chapter 15. Drug Addiction & The Brain's Reward Circuits: Chemicals That Harm with Pleasure, pp. 380-405 15.1 Basic Principles of Drug Action 15.2 Role of Learning in Drug Tolerance and Withdrawal 15.3 Five Commonly Abused Drugs 15.4 Biopsychological Theories of Addiction 15.5 Intracranial Self-Stimulation and the Pleasure Centers of the Brain 15.6 Neural Mechanisms of Motivation and Addiction 15.7 A Noteworthy Case of Addiction	**Instructor's Manual for** *BIOPSYCHOLOGY,* *Lecture 15a and Lecture 15b* **Test Bank for** *BIOPSYCHOLOGY,* *Chapter 15* **Study Guide for** *BIOPSYCHOLOGY,* *Chapter 15* **Transparencies for Physiological Psychology:** *XII. Neural Bases of Reward & Drug Abuse*	**Beyond the Brain & Behavior CD for** *BIOPSYCHOLOGY: Thinking About Drugs module* *Practice Tests for Chapter 15* *Hard Copy for Chapter 15* *Electronic Flashcards for Chapter 15* **Digital Image Archive, PowerPoint Presentation and Bitmap Images for** *BIOPSYCHOLOGY: Chapter 13* ***BIOLOGICAL PSYCHOLOGY VIDEO:*** *Segment 11. How Nicotine, Cocaine & Marijuana Affect the Brain*	

Lecture 15a

PRINCIPLES OF DRUG ACTION

Outline

1. The Drug Problem

2. Routes of Drug Administration

3. Mechanisms of Psychoactive Drug Action

4. Drug Tolerance & Withdrawal

5. Role of Learning in Drug Tolerance and Withdrawal
    a. Contingent Drug Tolerance
    b. Conditioned Drug Tolerance
    c. Conditioned Withdrawal
    d. Thinking about Drug Conditioning

Lecture Notes

1. The Drug Problem

-   60 million people in the USA alone are addicted to **alcohol, nicotine** or both; 5.5 million are addicted to **illegal drugs** and millions more are addicted to **prescription drugs**
-   it is important to note at the outset that the legal status of a drug says nothing about its safety or the health risks associated with it...for the most part, a drug's legal status was determined before we knew much about the risks associated with it

2. Routes of Drug Administration

-   drugs are consumed by people in the following ways:

-   **Ingestion:** preferred route of administration for many drugs; convenient but several major drawbacks including the unpredictability of absorption from the stomach or small intestine (absorption can be greatly influenced by food in the stomach) and fact that some drugs are deactivated before they can be absorbed from the digestive tract; most drugs are absorbed from the **small intestine,** but (e.g., alcohol) can be absorbed through the stomach wall, and thus they act more rapidly

-   **Injection; SC, IM,** or **IV**; favored route in medical practice because effects of injected drugs are **strong, fast** and **predictable;** in particular, addicts favor the IV route, but it is particularly dangerous as there is an increased risk of death from **overdose,** impure drugs, or allergic reactions; there are only a few sites on the body appropriate for IV injection, thus addicts frequently develop infections and scar tissue at these sites

-   **Inhalation:** many inhaled chemicals are **absorbed directly** into the bloodstream from the lungs (e.g., chemicals in tobacco and marijuana smoke); shortcomings include fact that dose is hard to regulate and lung damage is a serious risk from the repeated inhalation of chemicals

-   **Absorption:** through **mucous membranes;** some drugs (e.g., **cocaine**) are readily absorbed through the mucous membranes of the nose, mouth, or rectum; this method of administration is problematic as these membranes can be **easily damaged**

-   the **blood-brain barrier** makes it difficult for many drugs to enter the CNS

3.   **Mechanisms of Psychoactive Drug Action**

-    once a psychoactive drug has penetrated the CNS, it can influence neural activity in numerous ways; e.g., it can act diffusely on **neural membranes** or interact specifically with particular classes of **neurotransmitters** and **receptors**
-    the effects of most psychoactive drugs are terminated by their **metabolism,** i.e., by their conversion to nonactive **metabolites**; most drugs are metabolized by **liver enzymes**; in general, only small amounts of unmetabolized active drugs are eliminated in sweat, breath, urine, etc.

4.   **Drug Tolerance and Withdrawal** (see Fig. 15.1 and Fig. 15.2 in *BIOPSYCHOLOGY;* use *Digital Image Archive Figure CH13F02.BMP)*

-    **drug tolerance** is a state of decreased sensitivity to a drug's effect that results from prior exposure to the drug
-    tolerance can be measured in two ways: (1) by measuring the **decrease in the response** elicited by the same dose of the drug, or (2) by measuring the **increase in the amount of drug** required to produce the same effect; in effect, drug tolerance is a shift in the **dose-response curve** to the right
-    exposure to one drug can lead to the development of tolerance to another drug's effects **(cross tolerance)**
-    tolerance does not develop **equally** to all of the effects of a drug; indeed, **sensitization** can develop to some drug effects at the same time that tolerance can develop to other drug effects
-    there are multiple physiological mechanisms that can underlie a given form to drug tolerance; however, it is common to think of tolerance effects as being of two different types:

    i)   **Metabolic Tolerance** (any tolerance effect that results from a decrease in the amount of the drug reaching the target cells); or

    ii)   **Functional Tolerance** (any tolerance that results from a decrease in the ability of the drug to influence the target cells)

-    tolerance to most psychoactive drugs is primarily functional; it may be due to several types of neural changes, including changes in the **number of receptors** it binds to or the way it interacts with those receptors
-    after significant amounts of drug have been in the body for a period of time, its sudden elimination can trigger an illness called a **drug withdrawal syndrome;** these are usually opposite to the initial effects of the drug; when someone suffers from withdrawal symptoms if they stop taking a drug, they are said to be **physically dependent** on the drug
-    tolerance and withdrawal are thought to be different manifestations of the **same underlying physiological change;** when the drug is removed, the physiological changes that **compensate** for a drug's effects on the nervous system that are the basis of tolerance are no longer held in check by the drug, and withdrawal symptoms opposite to the original effects of the drug are the result
-    in general, longer drug exposure and more rapid elimination of a drug lead to greater withdrawal effects
-    **addicts** are habitual drug users who continue to use a drug despite its adverse effects on their health and social life, and despite repeated attempts to stop using it
-    **addiction does not equal physical dependence**

5.   **Role of Learning in Drug Tolerance and Withdrawal** (see Fig. 15.3 - Fig. 15.5 in *BIOPSYCHOLOGY;* use *Digital Image Archive Figure CH13F04.BMP* and *CH13F05.BMP)*

-    3 lines of research have shown that learning can influence the development of tolerance or withdrawal to a drug's effects: demonstrations of **contingent drug tolerance, conditioned drug tolerance** and **conditioned drug withdrawal**

a. Contingent Drug Tolerance

- contingent drug tolerance is tolerance that develops only to drug effects that are actually **experienced**
- it is usually demonstrated by **before-and-after experiments**
- in before-and-after experiments, the subjects in one condition (the **drug-before-test condition**) are tested after each injection so that they repeatedly experience the effect of the drug on the test behavior
- the subjects in the other condition (the **drug-after-test condition**) are tested before each injection so that they do not repeatedly experience the drug's effect on the test behavior
- the typical finding in such experiments is that the development of tolerance is substantially greater in the drug-before-test condition than in the drug-after-test condition
- for example, Pinel et al. demonstrated contingent tolerance to the anticonvulsant effect of ethanol
- during the **tolerance-development phase** of this experiment, the rats in the **ethanol-before** group received an ethanol injection once every 48 hours, 1 hour before a convulsive amygdala stimulation, thus they repeatedly experienced ethanol's anticonvulsant effect
- the rats in the **ethanol-after** group received ethanol injections on the same bi-daily schedule, but 1 hour after each convulsive stimulation, thus they never experienced ethanol's anticonvulsant effect
- on the test day, only the rats in the **ethanol-before-stimulation group** were tolerant to alcohol's anticonvulsant effect

b. Conditioned Drug Tolerance

- **conditioned drug tolerance** refers to tolerance that is maximally expressed in the presence of **drug-predictive stimuli**
- for example; Crowell, Hinson, and Siegel (1981) demonstrated conditioned tolerance to the **hypothermic effect** of alcohol. In this study, two groups of rats received 20 alcohol injections and 20 saline injections in alternating sequence, one every 48 hours.
- the only difference between the two groups was that the rats in one group always received their alcohol in a distinctive test room and their saline in their colony room, whereas the rats in the other group received their saline in the test room and their alcohol in the colony room
- remarkably, tolerance to the hypothermic effect of alcohol was revealed only when the subjects were tested in the same environment in which they had previously received alcohol
- according to Siegel, Hinson, Krank, and McCully (1982), addicts develop tolerance to drug effects that are repeatedly experienced in the same environment and consequently they must start taking larger doses of the drug to maintain the effects that they see; however, when they take the elevated dose in a novel environment in which they are not tolerant, they run the risk of a **drug overdose**
- in support of this hypothesis, Siegel et al. showed that rats were more susceptible to the lethal effects of a heroin overdose if they received the injection in an environment different from that in which they had experienced the effects of previous drug injections
- one theory of the situational specificity of tolerance is Siegel's **conditioned compensatory response theory**
- Siegel proposed that each incidence of drug administration is like a Pavlovian conditioning trial; the drug effect is the UCS, which is preceded on each trial by the drug-predictive environment that serves as the CS
- as conditioning occurs, the drug-predictive environmental CS begins to elicit CRs that are opposite to the effects of the drug; these **conditioned compensatory responses**--as Siegel termed them--offset the effects of the drug, and tolerance is the consequence
- it is also possible for **conditioned sensitization** to develop to a drug's effects; for example, the administration of amphetamine every 3-4 days for a total of 10 injections, greatly increases the sensitivity of rats to subsequent amphetamine injections…but only if those injections are administered in the same environment in which they had experienced the previous amphetamine injections

c. Conditioned Withdrawal Effects

- these are withdrawal effects that are elicited by the **drug environment** or other **drug-associated cues**
- according to Seigel and his colleagues, they reflect the expression of a conditioned response to drug-predictive cues in the **absence of the drug** itself
- for example, Krank and Perkins (1993) found that rats that were tested for opiate withdrawal symptoms in the same environment that they had experienced the drug in the past experienced more withdrawal symptoms than rats with the same drug history that were assessed for withdrawal in a novel environment or than drug-naïve rats.

d. Thinking About Drug Conditioning

- conditioned drug effects are inevitable in any situation in which drugs are repeatedly administered; however, it is difficult to predict whether the conditioned response will **complement** the drug's effects (and produce **conditioned sensitization**) or **oppose** the drug's effects (and produce **conditioned tolerance**).
- this unpredictability may reflect confusion on the part of researchers about the nature of the US and the UR; Ramsay and Woods (1997) have argued that the drug's effects on the nervous system are the US (not the drug per se), and the UR reflects the response of the nervous system to the drug's effects
- in most cases, the UR opposes the drug's effects and thus the development of a CR leads conditioned tolerance
- in some cases, however, the UR complements the drug's effects and thus the development of a CR leads conditioned sensitization

Suggested Websites for Lecture 15a

Behavioral Factors in Drug Tolerance: *http://www.nida.nih.gov/pdf/monographs/download18.html*
A classic monograph from Dr. N.A. Krasnegor and NIDA.

An Overview of Drug Tolerance:
http://salmon.psy.plym.ac.uk/year3/psy337drugtolerance/drugtolerance.htm
From Dr. Paul Kenyon's award-winning SALMON site, a good overview of the basics of drug tolerance.

Lecture 15b

DRUG ADDICTION, REWARDING BRAIN STIMULATION, AND THE
MESOTELENCEPHALIC DOPAMINE SYSTEM

Outline

1. Five Commonly Abused Drugs
    a. Tobacco
    b. Alcohol
    c. Marijuana
    d. Cocaine
    e. The Opiates

2. Theories of Addiction
    f. Physical-Dependence Theories
    g. Positive-Incentive Theories

3. Intracranial Self-Stimulation (ICSS)
    a. Fundamental Features of ICSS
    b. Mesotelencephalic Dopamine System

4. Neural Mechanisms of Motivation and Addiction

Lecture Notes

1. **Five Commonly Abused Drugs** (see Fig. 15.6 in *BIOPSYCHOLOGY;* use *Biological Psychology Video, Segment 11. How Nicotine, Cocaine and Marijuana Affect the Brain)*

    a) **Tobacco:**

    -   is used more than any other drug except caffeine; about 76 million Americas currently use tobacco products
    -   usually inhaled or absorbed through oral mucosa
    -   **nicotine** is the major psychoactive ingredient; 4,000 other known chemicals are in tobacco
    -   tobacco is **highly addictive;** for example, about 70% of people who try tobacco products end up addicted (as opposed to 10% for ethanol or 30% for heroin
    -   addictive properties highlighted by behavior of patients with **Buerger's disease;** they will still smoke, even after their limbs are amputated because of smoking-related vasoconstriction and gangrene
    -   effects of tobacco range from nausea, vomiting and diarrhea in new tobacco users to feelings of relaxation and alertness in experienced smokers
    -   consequences of smoking include chest pain, coughing, failure of the cardiorespiratory system, and cancer; this can also apply to victims of second-hand smoke

    b) **Alcohol:**

    -   is consumed by 66% of the US population and 13 million are addicted
    -   is widely distributed, as it is both fat and water soluble
    -   is classified as a **depressant,** though at low doses it can actually stimulate neural activity
    -   can change brain activity by reducing the movement of calcium ions across the neural membrane; by interfering with second-messenger systems; or by disrupting **GABAergic** or **glutamatergic** neurotransmission

- at moderate doses, alcohol impairs **cognitive, perceptual, verbal** and **motor skills;** high doses result in a lack of consciousness, and very high doses can be lethal due to respiratory depression
- can produce **tolerance** and **physical dependence;** heavy drinkers are able to metabolize more alcohol than nondrinkers, though most tolerance is **functional**
- the withdrawal syndrome can range from the **headache** and **nausea** of a **hangover** to **severe tremors, nausea, hallucinations, convulsions,** and **delirium tremens (DT's);** the last 2 withdrawal symptoms can be severe enough to be fatal
- alcohol attacks all body tissues, including the **brain** (e.g., **Korsakoff's syndrome**); severe scarring or **cirrhosis** of the liver can result from long-term alcohol abuse
- alcohol also crosses the placenta and can result in birth defects such as **Fetal Alcohol Syndrome.**

c) Marijuana:

- elicits psychoactive responses largely due to **THC** (delta-9-tetrahydrocannabinol)
- **long history** of use by human beings
- may be **inhaled** or ingested **orally** (usually baked into an oil-rich substrate to aid absorption)
- at social doses, marijuana has subtle effects that range from an increased sense of **well-being, craving sweets,** and **enhanced sensations;** higher doses can lead to **impaired judgment** and **short-term memory impairment**
- marijuana elicits its CNS effects at **cannabinoid receptors** in the brain; these are especially common in the **basal ganglia, cerebellum** and **hippocampus;** these receptors are believed to bind the endogenous THC-like chemical called **anadamide**
- a possible negative consequence is **lung damage** due to inhaling the drug; in addition, there is some evidence that marijuana can exacerbate **cardiovascular problems;** the problem of a marijuana **amotivational syndrome** does not seem to supported by the literature
- the **addiction potential** of marijuana is **low,** as is the likelihood of experiencing significant withdrawal symptoms after chronically ingesting marijuana
- clinically, marijuana has been shown to block the nausea of cancer drugs, stimulate appetite, and decrease the severity of **glaucoma**

d) Cocaine and other stimulants:

- have the **same general effect,** but differ greatly in their **potency**
- **cocaine** may be inhaled, absorbed across mucosal membranes, or injected
- cocaine is very addictive; however, its withdrawal syndrome is relatively mild
- cocaine acts by blocking **catecholamine reuptake;** its euphoria-inducing properties seem to be due to its effects on dopaminergic neurotransmission
- cocaine is a general stimulant, producing a feeling of **energy, well-being,** and **self-confidence;** extremely high doses can lead to **cocaine psychosis** characterized by **sleeplessness, nausea, restlessness** and **psychotic behavior;** in addition, high doses can produce **stroke, seizures,** and **respiratory arrest**
- considerable attention has been paid to the possible effects of cocaine on **prenatal development;** it appears that cocaine abuse by expectant mothers can significantly **retard the cognitive development** of the child, but not to the extent that the popular press has described
- clinically, cocaine derivatives are effective as **local anesthetics**
- **amphetamine** and related compounds like **methamphetamine** are also commonly abused stimulants

e) The Opiates:

- include **morphine, codeine** and **heroin**
- these are unmatched as **analgesics** and are **very addictive;** over 130,000 Americans currently use heroin
- key addictive effects seem to be a rush of **pleasure** and **drowsy euphoria; tolerance** develops to these effects, meaning that addicts must administer very high doses to get the desired effect
- a **withdrawal syndrome** appears within hours of the last dose; although the symptoms are not trivial, they are not as bad as the popular press would have us believe and seem to be similar to a bad case of the flu

- undesirable side effects include **constipation, pupil constriction,** and **reduced libido**
- outside of IV transmitted diseases and problems, very **few health risks** are seen in users
- opiates elicit their effects on the CNS by acting at receptors in the brain that normally bind **endogenous opiates** (also called **endorphins**)

2. Biopsychological Theories of Addiction

- the critical question in this area is: Do addicts abuse a drug because they are trying to fulfill an internal need, or are they drawn by the anticipated positive effect of the drug

a. Physical-Dependence Theories of Addiction

- early attempts to explain addiction attributed it to **physical dependence;** addicts take drugs to curtail the **withdrawal symptoms** that they otherwise would face
- from this perspective, treating addiction meant withdrawal from the drug in a hospital setting until the symptoms subsided
- unfortunately, addicts almost always return to drug taking after they have been released from hospital
- the failure of this treatment approach is not surprising in the light of two well-established facts about drug taking:
  - i) some highly addictive drugs produce little withdrawal distress (e.g., cocaine); and
  - ii) the pattern of drug taking in many addicts typically involves self-imposed cycles of **binges** and **detoxification**
- modern **physical-dependence theories** of addiction attempt to account for the inevitability of relapse after detoxification by postulating that withdrawal effects can be **conditioned**
- there are two problems with this theory:

  - **i)** many of the conditioned effects elicited by drug-taking environments are similar to the effects of the drug, not to the drug's withdrawal effects; and
  - **ii)** addicts and experimental animals often find drug-related cues rewarding, even in the absence of the drug (e.g., **needle freaks** enjoy sticking empty hypodermic needles in their arms)

b. Positive-Incentive Theories of Addiction

- the failings of physical-dependence theories have lent support to **positive-incentive theories**; according to positive-incentive theories of addiction, most addicts take drugs to obtain their pleasurable effects rather than to escape their aversive aftereffects
- Robinson and Berridge (1993) have suggested that the expectation of the pleasurable effects of drugs may become **sensitized** in addicts; a key point of this **incentive-sensitization** theory is that addicts don't receive more pleasure from the drug, it is the **anticipated pleasure** that motivates their behavior; thus, in drug addicts the craving for a drug may be out of proportion with the pleasure that they actually derive from taking it

3. Intracranial Self-Stimulation (ICSS) (see Fig. 15.7 – Fig. 15.9 in *BIOPSYCHOLOGY;* use *Digital Image Archive Figure CH13F09.BMP - CH13F11.BMP)*

- ICSS was discovered by accident in the early 1950s by Olds and Milner
- although animals self-stimulate a variety of brain structures, most studies in the 1950s and 1960s focused on the **septum** and **lateral hypothalamus** because the self-stimulation rates at these sites are impressively high

a. Fundamental Features of ICSS

- early studies suggested that lever pressing for brain stimulation was fundamentally different from lever pressing for food or water; ICSS was often characterized by extremely **high response rates, rapid extinction,** and **priming**

- these and other differences appeared to discredit Olds and Milner's original premise that animals self-stimulate sites that activate natural reward circuits (e.g., circuits that normally mediate the rewarding effects of food, water, sex, etc.)
- the pendulum of scientific opinion has swung as evidence has accumulated linking intracranial self-stimulation to **natural reward mechanisms**
- four lines of evidence have linked intracranial self-stimulation to natural reward mechanisms:

    i) in the presence of the appropriate goal objects, stimulation at positive self-stimulation sites often elicits **natural motivated behaviors** such as eating, drinking, and copulation;
    ii) increasing levels of natural motivation (e.g., by food or water deprivation) often **increases self-stimulation rates;**
    iii) self-stimulation at sites other than the septum and lateral hypothalamus is frequently similar to lever pressing for natural reinforcers (e.g., slower response rates, slower extinction, no priming); and
    iv) subtle differences between the paradigm used to assess lever pressing for natural reinforcers and the paradigm used to assess lever pressing for brain stimulation contributed to the impression that the rewarding effects of brain stimulation and those of natural reinforcers were fundamentally different

- Panksepp and Trowill (1967) pointed out that in contrast to rats' lever pressing for food, self-stimulating rats are not deprived and they don't have to perform an additional **consummatory response** (e.g., eating) after each lever press to obtain the reinforcement
- Panksepp and Trowill showed that nondeprived rats' lever pressing to inject small amounts of chocolate milk directly into their mouths through an implanted tube, performed remarkably like self-stimulating rats: they learned very rapidly to lever press, they extinguished almost immediately, and some even had to be primed

b. Mesotelencephalic Dopamine System

- a variety of neural circuits can mediate self-stimulation but one neural system that appears to play a particularly important role is **the mesotelencephalic dopamine system**
- the mesotelencephalic dopamine system ascends from two mesencephalic dopaminergic nuclei: the **substantia nigra** and the **ventral tegmental area**
- most of the axons of substantia nigra neurons terminate in the striatum and are commonly referred to as the **nigrostriatal pathway;** these neurons degenerate in patients with Parkinson's disease
- the axons of ventral tegmental area neurons project to the limbic system and cortex and are commonly referred to as the **mesocortical limbic pathway**; this pathway appears to be most important to the rewarding effects of **natural reinforcers, brain stimulation,** and **drugs**
- four kinds of evidence support the notion that the mesocorticolimbic dopamine system plays a particularly important role in self-stimulation:

    i) **Mapping Studies:** areas that support ICSS are typically part of the mesotelencephalic dopamine system or else project there;
    ii) *In vivo* **Cerebral Microdialysis Studies:** there is an increase in the release of dopamine from the mesocorticolimbic dopamine system when an animal is engaged in ICSS;
    iii) **Dopamine Agonist and Antagonist Studies:** dopamine agonists increase ICSS and dopamine antagonists decrease ICSS; and
    iv) **Lesion Studies:** lesions of the mesotelencephalic dopamine system disrupt ICSS.

4. **Neural Mechanisms of Motivation and Addiction** (see Fig. 15.10 in *BIOPSYCHOLOGY;* use *Digital Image Archive Figure CH13F12.BMP)*

- the most **isomorphic** animal model of human addiction is the **drug self-administration paradigm** *(use Digital Image Archive Figure CH13F12.BMP);* animals will self-administer many addictive drugs, often mimicking many of the drug-taking behaviors characteristic of human addicts

- the **conditioned place-preference paradigm** is also used to examine the rewarding effects of drugs
- during the conditioning phase, rats repeatedly receive a drug in the **drug compartment** of a **two-compartment box**
- during testing, drug-free rats are placed in the box and the proportion of time spent in the compartment where it used to receive the drug is compared to time spent in the control compartment
- during drug-free testing rats spend more time in the **drug compartment**
- using ICSS, self-administration and place-preference conditioning paradigms, investigators have established four major lines of evidence support the view that the mesotelencephalic dopamine system, particularly mesocorticolimbic terminals in the **nucleus accumbens**, mediates the rewarding effects of drugs as well as the effects of natural reinforcers:

   i) laboratory animals **self-administer** microinjections of addictive drugs into the nucleus accumbens;
   ii) microinjections of drugs into the nucleus accumbens lead to the development of **conditioned place-preferences;**
   iii) destruction of the VTA or the nucleus accumbens has been shown to block self-administration or the development of conditioned place preferences; and
   iv) self-administration of addictive drugs or natural reinforcers are both associated with increased dopamine release in the nucleus accumbens.

- recent research suggests that dopamine release in the nucleus accumbens plays a key role in the **anticipation** of reward, rather than in the experience of reward itself; for example, dopamine is released in the nucleus accumbens when a tone signaling a reward is presented, rather than when the reward itself is presented
- researchers are now studying the nucleus accumbens, and its connections with the **amygdala** and **prefrontal cortex**, to learn more about the role of these structures in the development of drug addiction

Suggested Websites for Lecture 15b:

Ethanol: *http://www.dana.org/articles/dbk_0298.cfm*
From the Dana Foundation, an overview of the effects of ethanol on the nervous system.

Heroin: *http://www.nida.nih.gov/ResearchReports/Heroin/Heroin.html*
From NIDA, a monograph on heroin/opiate addiction.

Marijuana: *http://www.nida.nih.gov/Infofax/marijuana.html*
General information about the health consequences of marijuana; good recent statistics.

Nicotine: *http://www.nida.nih.gov/ResearchReports/Nicotine/Nicotine.html*
From NIDA, a monograph on nicotine; simply written, many up-to-date statistics.

Brookhaven National Laboratory's Images of Addiction: *http://www.pet.bnl.gov/images.html*
A collection of animations, PET images, and other images illustrating the effects of cocaine, nicotine, and other drugs of abuse on the brain. Highly recommended

Neural Substrates for Drugs of Abuse: *http://www.nida.nih.gov/Teaching/teaching4.html*
From NIDA, a nice set of slides showing the effects of cocaine, opiates and marijuana on the brain.

Neural Bases of Addiction:
   http://www.med.harvard.edu/publications/On_The_Brain/Volume2/Special/SPAdd.html
An interview with Dr. Steven Hyman and Dr. Howard Shaffer on the neural bases of addiction; from Harvard University's Mahoney Neuroscience Institute.

**IM-AT-A-GLANCE: Chapter 16. Lateralization, Language and the Split Brain:
The Left Brain and the Right Brain of Language**

Detailed Outline	Print Supplements	Media Supplements	Professor's Notes
Chapter 16. Lateralization, Language and the Split Brain: The Left Brain and the Right Brain of Language, pp. 406-436 16.1　Cerebral Lateralization of Function: Introduction 16.2　The Split Brain 16.3　Differences between the Left and Right Hemispheres 16.4　Cortical Localization of Language: The Wernicke-Geschwind Model 16.5　Evaluation of the Wernicke-Geshwind Model 16.6　The Cognitive Neuroscience Approach to Language 16.7　The Cognitive Neuroscience Approach and Dyslexia	**Instructor's Manual for** *BIOPSYCHOLOGY,* *Lecture 16a and Lecture 16b* **Test Bank for** *BIOPSYCHOLOGY,* *Chapter 16* **Study Guide for** *BIOPSYCHOLOGY,* *Chapter 16* **Transparencies for Physiological Psychology:** *XII. Language and Localization of Function*	**Beyond the Brain & Behavior CD for** *BIOPSYCHOLOGY:* *Practice Tests for Chapter 16* *Hard Copy for Chapter 16* *Electronic Flashcards for Chapter 16* **Digital Image Archive, PowerPoint Presentation and Bitmap Images for** *BIOPSYCHOLOGY:* *Chapter 16* ***BIOLOGICAL PSYCHOLOGY VIDEO:*** *Segment 14. How The Brain Processes Language*	

Lecture 16a

LATERALIZATION AND THE SPLIT BRAIN

Outline

1. Aphasia and Apraxia: The Dominant Left Hemisphere

2. Tests of Cerebral Lateralization
    a. Sodium Amytal Test
    b. Dichotic Listening Test
    c. Functional Brain Imaging

3. The Ground-Breaking Split-Brain Experiment of Myers and Sperry

4. Tests of Split-Brain Patients
    a. Evidence of Two Independent Streams of Consciousness
    b. Cross Cuing
    c. Learning Two Things at Once
    d. Helping-Hand Phenomenon

5. Differences Between the Left and Right Hemispheres

6. Three Theories of Cerebral Asymmetry
    a. Analytic-Synthesis Theory
    b. Motor Theory
    c. Linguistic Theory

Lecture Notes

1. **Aphasia and Apraxia: The Dominant Left Hemisphere** (see Fig. 16.2 in *BIOPSYCHOLOGY;* use *Digital Image Archive Figure CH16F02.BMP)*

    -   in 1836, **Dax,** an unknown country doctor, reported that not one of his 40 or so patients with speech problems had displayed damage restricted to the right hemisphere; his report attracted no interest
    -   25 years later, **Broca** reported the results of the postmortem examination of two **aphasic** patients (patients with deficits in the use of language that are not attributable to general sensory, motor, or intellectual dysfunction); both had diffuse **left hemisphere damage** that seemed to be centered in an area of the inferior left prefrontal lobe, just in front of the primary motor face area
    -   in the next few years, Broca examined 7 more brains of deceased aphasic patients; all had damage that included the same left frontal area, which became known as **Broca's area**
    -   subsequently, **Liepmann** discovered that **apraxia** (difficulty performing movements with either side of the body when asked to do so, but not when performing them spontaneously) was almost always associated with left hemisphere damage
    -   this led to the view that all complex activities were performed by the left hemisphere; the left and right hemispheres thus became known as the **dominant** and **minor** hemispheres, respectively

2. **Tests of Cerebral Lateralization**

    -   the first evidence of language laterality came from comparisons of the effects of left and right **unilateral lesions**; today, the **sodium amytal test** and the **dichotic listening test** are commonly used to assess language laterality

    a. **Sodium Amytal Test**

- the sodium amytal test is administered to patients prior to neurosurgery so that the surgeon knows the side of speech lateralization and can take special care to avoid damaging the language areas
- a small amount of **sodium amytal** is injected into one **carotid artery**; this anesthetizes the **ipsilateral** hemisphere and allows the abilities of the **contralateral** hemisphere to be assessed
- when the injection is made on the side of the **dominant speech hemisphere** (usually the left), the patient is totally **mute** for a minute or two, and as the ability to talk returns the patient makes speech errors (e.g., errors of naming and serial order)
- when the injection is on the side of the **nondominant speech hemisphere** (usually the right), there is no mutism and only a few speech errors

b. Dichotic Listening Test

- in the conventional form of the dichotic listening test, a sequence of three pairs of digits is presented through ear phones; the two digits of each pair are presented simultaneously, one digit to each ear
- when the subject is asked to report the 6 digits that she or he has heard, there is a slight but consistent tendency to report more of the digits presented to the ear contralateral to the dominant language hemisphere (usually the right ear)

c. Functional Brain Imaging

- PET or fMRI techniques have revealed that there is typically more activity in the left hemisphere than the right during language-related activities

- many studies have reported a relation between speech laterality and handedness; the following general conclusions have been reached:

i)   nearly all (about 95%) right-handed subjects are left-hemisphere dominant for speech;
ii)   most left-handed or ambidextrous subjects (about 70%) are also left-hemisphere dominant for speech; and
iii) early left-hemisphere damage can cause the right hemisphere to become dominant for speech and the left hand to be preferred

- there is some evidence that the brain is more lateralized in males than in females, although the data are hardly unequivocal

3. The Ground-Breaking Split-Brain Experiment of Myers and Sperry (see Fig. 16.1, Fig.16.3 and Fig. 16.4 in *BIOPSYCHOLOGY;* use *Digital Image Archive Figure CH16F01.BMP* and *CH16F05.BMP)*

- in 1953, Myers and Sperry performed an experiment on cats that changed the way that we think about the brain; and it provided a means of comparing the functions of the two hemispheres
- it was an experiment designed to reveal the function of the brain's largest **commissure**, the **corpus callosum**
- the corpus callosum is the largest tract in the human brain, contains approximately 200 million axons, and it is the highest level at which the two cerebral hemispheres are connected
- on the basis of its size and location, one would think that severing it would have devastating consequences; however, many earlier studies had failed to reveal any deficits in laboratory animals following **callosal transection,** and people born without a corpus callosum had been reported to be perfectly normal (leading some neuroscientists to joke that its job was to keep the cortex out of the ventricles!); Sperry was intrigued by the paradox
- in 1953, Myers and Sperry's published a groundbreaking paper that solved this apparent paradox. In their experiment, there were four groups of cats: (1) **corpus callosum** severed, (2) **optic chiasm** severed, (3) **corpus callosum and optic chiasm** severed, and (4) intact controls
- in phase 1 of the experiment, all cats learned a lever-press pattern discrimination task with a **patch** over one eye; all four groups readily learned this simple task
- in phase 2, the patch was **switched** to the other eye; the cats in the optic-chiasm-severed group, in the corpus-callosum-severed group, and in the control group kept performing at close to 100% when the patch was shifted; in contrast, the cats with both their optic chiasms and corpus callosums severed, acted as if the task were completely new to them--they had to **learn it again** with no savings

- Meyers and Sperry concluded:

  - i) the cat forebrain has the capacity to act as **two separate forebrains,** each capable of **independent learning** and of storing its own memories;
  - ii) the function of the corpus callosum is to **carry information between hemispheres;**
  - iii) the best strategy for studying corpus callosum function is to use a method to limit information to a single hemisphere (e.g., by cutting the optic chiasm and blindfolding one eye)

4. **Tests of Split-Brain Patients** (see Fig. 16.5 and Fig. 16.6 in *BIOPSYCHOLOGY;* use *Digital Image Archive Figure CH16F06.BMP)*

    - **commissurotomy** is performed on patients with life-threatening cases of epilepsy to reduce the severity of convulsions by restricting epileptic discharges to half the brain
    - the operation is **remarkably effective;** many commissurotomized epileptic patients never experience another major convulsion; more remarkably they experience few obvious side effects in their daily lives
    - the controlled neuropsychological testing of these split-brain patients has revealed some amazing things about the human brain; the testing of the initial series of patients was conducted by Sperry and Gazzaniga
    - to test split-brain patients, visual stimuli were flashed (to eliminate the effect of eye movement) on a screen to the left or right of a **fixation point** for **0.1 seconds** (contrast this method of limiting visual input to one hemisphere with the method used by Myers and Sperry in cats)
    - tactual information was presented to one hand under a ledge or in a bag to prevent visual scanning of the objects; responses were either verbal responses or manual responses performed by one hand or the other under a ledge
    - amazingly, these tests confirmed the provocative conclusions of the experiments on split-brain laboratory animals in showing that the commissurotomized patients had **two independent streams of consciousness;** however, unlike split-brain laboratory animals the two hemispheres of commissurotomized patients were **not equal**; e.g., the left hemisphere could speak but the right could not

    a. **Evidence of Two Independent Streams of Consciousness**
        - when an object was presented to the **left hemisphere**, either by touching with the right hand or by viewing something in the right visual field, the subject could: i) pick out the correct object with the right hand, ii) could not pick out the correct object with the left hand, iii) could name the correct object
        - when an object was presented to the **right hemisphere**, either by touching with the left hand or by viewing something in the left visual field, the subject: i) could pick out the correct object with the left hand, ii) could not pick out the correct object with the right hand, iii) claimed nothing had been presented
        - if you are having difficulty understanding these results because you are used to thinking of yourself as an indivisible entity; think of each person as two subjects: (1) **Mr. or Ms. Right Hemisphere** who understands a few simple instructions but cannot speak, who receives sensory information from the left visual field and left hand, and who controls the fine motor responses of the left hand; and (2) **Mr. or Ms. Left Hemisphere** who understands complex speech and can speak, who receives sensory information from the right-visual field and right hand, and who controls the fine motor responses of the right hand

    b. **Cross-Cuing**
        - **cross-cuing** represents communication between hemispheres via a nonneural route
        - for example, in one test, a red or a green light was flashed in the left visual field; the split-brain patient was then asked to name the color: red or green
        - most split-brain patients get 50% correct on this task, however one patient eventually developed the ability to perform almost perfectly
        - when the performance of this subject was carefully observed, it was noticed that on the trials when the patient initially said (the left hemisphere) the incorrect color, his head shook, and the patient then changed his guess to the other, correct color; apparently, the right hemisphere (who knew the correct answer) heard the incorrect guess of the left hemisphere, and signaled to the left hemisphere that it was wrong by shaking the person's head; when only first guesses were counted, performance immediately fell to 50%

c. **Learning Two Things at Once**
  - split-brain patients are capable of learning two things at once
  - if a split-brain patient is visually presented with two objects at the same time--let's say a pencil in the left visual field and an apple in the right--she or he can reach into two different bags at the same time, one with each hand, and pull out the two objects--a pencil in the left hand and an apple in the right
  - What would a split-brain subject say in this example if she were asked what she had in her hands before withdrawing them from the bags? ("two apples")

d. **Helping-Hand Phenomenon**
  - an interesting phenomenon, called the **helping-hand phenomenon**, occurs when the two hemispheres are presented with different information about the correct choice and then are asked to reach out and pick up the correct object from a collection in full view
  - usually the right hand will reach out to pick out what the left hemisphere saw (i.e., the apple in our previous example), but the right hemisphere seeing what it thinks is an error being made causes the left hand to grab the right hand and pull it over to the other object (i.e., the pencil in our previous example)

5. **Differences Between the Left and Right Hemispheres** (see Table 16.1 and Fig. 16.7 and Fig. 16.8 in *BIOPSYCHOLOGY;* use *Digital Image Archive Figure CH16F08.BMP, CH16F09.BMP* and *CH16FTB.BMP)*

  - language is the most lateralized of all abilities; the left hemisphere is better than the right at all **language-related tasks**; however, the right hemisphere proved to be able to understand written and spoken words and simple grammatical principles; the various language abilities of the right hemisphere proved to be comparable to those of a normal preschool-aged child
  - the left hemisphere has also proved to be better at controlling **ipsilateral body movements**
  - the right hemisphere proved better than the left at a variety of tasks, most notably those involving **spatial ability** (e.g., block designs subtest of the WAIS; **stereognosis**)
  - the right hemisphere is also superior in processing **emotional stimuli** and for **musical tasks**
  - finally, the two hemispheres seem to engage different types of memory processing; the left hemisphere attempts to place its experiences in a **larger context,** while the right hemisphere attends strictly to the **perceptual characteristics** of the stimulus
  - thus, the right hemisphere should not be regarded as the minor hemisphere; it has **different abilities,** not less important ones
  - it is critical to keep in mind the idea that complex **clusters of cognitive abilities** (e.g., language) are **NOT lateralized;** instead, the **constituent cognitive processes** that underlie complex cognitive functions seem to be lateralized to one or the other hemisphere of the brain
  - there are also **anatomical asymmetries** in the human brain; for example, in the **planum temporale, Heschl's gyrus, and the frontal operculum**
  - all of these are language-related areas and might be expected to be larger in the left hemisphere, but in fact this is not so…the planum temporale and frontal operculum are usually larger on the left, but Heschl's gyrus is usually larger on the right

6. **Three Theories of Cerebral Asymmetry**

  - Why has cerebral asymmetry evolved? Three main theories have tried to account for cerebral asymmetry:

  a) **Analytic-Synthetic Theory:**

    - suggests that there are two fundamentally different modes of thinking, an **analytic mode** and a **synthetic mode,** and that the neural circuitry for each is fundamentally different
    - as a result, the two kinds of circuits are presumed to have become segregated during evolution, the analytic mode in the left hemisphere and the synthetic mode in the right
    - the left hemisphere, according to this theory, operates in a logical, sequential, analytic fashion; the right hemisphere makes immediate, overall synthetic judgments

b) Motor Theory:
- posits that the left hemisphere is specialized for **fine motor movement** of which speech is but one example
- two lines of evidence support this theory: (1) lesions of the left hemisphere disrupt facial movements more than do right hemisphere lesions, even when they are not related to speech; (2) the degree of disruption of nonverbal facial movements is positively correlated with the degree of aphasia

c) Linguistic Theory:
- is based on the idea that the primary function of the left hemisphere is language; this is based on studies of deaf people who communicate using American Sign Language; this ability is lost if these people suffer damage to the left hemisphere, even when they are able to make the movements required.

Suggested Websites for Lecture 16a:

The Corpus Callosum: *http://www.indiana.edu/~pietsch/callosum.html*
From Paul Pietsch's *Shuffle Brain*, an examination of the corpus callosum; great figures, good text, links to related research.

Laterality in Primates: *http://www.indiana.edu/~primate/index.html*
An informative page from M.K. Holder at the University of Indiana on handedness and laterality of function; in particular, see:

http://www.indiana.edu/~primate/brain.html

Nobel Prize and Sperry: *http://www.nobel.se/medicine/laureates/1981/sperry-autobio.html*
An autobiography for Roger Sperry, celebrating his Nobel Prize "for his discoveries concerning the functional specialization of the cerebral hemispheres"; be sure to check out the essay in honor of Sperry at this site.

Two Brains: *http://faculty.washington.edu/chudler/split.html*
From Dr. Eric Chudler's excellent site at the University of Washington, a great resource on split brains and laterality of function; good text and figures, and links to related sites on the Web.

Lecture 16b

CORTICAL LOCALIZATION OF LANGUAGE

Outline

1.   Historical Perspectives

2.   The Wernicke-Geschwind Model

3.   Tests of the Wernicke-Geschwind Model
     a. Surgical Lesions
     b. Brain Damage
     c. CAT Scans and MRI Scans
     d. Electrical Stimulation
     e. Current Status of the Wernicke-Geschwind Model

4.   The Cognitive Neuroscience Approach to Language

5.   The Cognitive Neuroscience Approach and Dyslexia

Lecture Notes

1.   **Historical Perspectives** (see Fig. 16.2 in *BIOPSYCHOLOGY;* use *Digital Image Archive Figure CH16F02.BMP)*

-   in 1864, **Broca** that the inferior portion of the left prefrontal lobe (**Broca's area**) is the center of speech production; he suggested that Broca's area controls the area of **primary motor cortex** that controls the muscles of the face and oral cavity
-   in 1874, Wernicke concluded on the basis of 10 clinical cases that the area in the left temporal lobe just posterior to the **primary auditory cortex** is another important language area; it became known as **Wernicke's area**
-   Wernicke's area was hypothesized by Wernicke to play a role in language comprehension; Wernicke claimed that damage to Broca's area produces **aphasia** that is primarily **expressive** (no deficits in language comprehension and speech that is meaningful, but slow, labored, disjointed, and poorly articulated)
-   by contrast, damage to Wernicke's area was hypothesized to produce aphasia that is primarily **receptive** (deficits in language comprehension and speech that has the structure, rhythm, and intonation of real speech but is incomprehensible--a **word salad**)
-   Wernicke also argued that damage to the left **arcuate fasciculus**, which connects Broca's and Wernicke's areas, should produce aphasia characterized by a difficulty in repeating words that were heard; he called this third hypothetical form of aphasia **conduction aphasia**

2.   **The Wernicke-Geschwind Model** (see Fig. 16.9 and Fig. 16.10 in *BIOPSYCHOLOGY;* use *Digital Image Archive Figure CH16F10.BMP* and *CH16F11.BMP;* use *Biological Psychology Video,* Segment 14. How the Brain Processes Language)

-   during the era of Broca and Wernicke, the most scholars did not favor **localizationist** models, and Broca's and Wernicke's hypotheses had little influence
-   however, in 1965 Norman Geschwind combined these ideas with Dejerine's (1892) conclusion that damage in the **angular gyrus** (on the border between the left temporal and parietal lobes, just anterior to the occipital lobe) is the cause of **alexia** and **agraphia**; the model of the cerebral control of language that resulted from Geschwind's synthesis is called the **Wernicke-Geschwind model**

- the main support for the model came from Geschwind's interpretation of his own aphasic patients; most of these cases had brain damage that was diffuse and often involved subcortical structures as well
- the Wernicke-Geschwind model was the dominant neuropsychological theory of language for over 20 years; however, it has not stood up well to the challenge of empirical testing by investigators other than Geschwind

3. **Tests of the Wernicke-Geschwind Model** (see Fig. 16.11 - Fig. 16.15 in *BIOPSYCHOLOGY;* use *Digital Image Archive Figure CH16F14.BMP* and *CH16F17.BMP)*

   a. **Surgical Lesions**

   - patients with **surgical lesions** are particularly useful for such studies because the site of their lesion is well known
   - in addition, patients rendered aphasic by accidental brain damage almost always have extensive **subcortical** damage, which leads to widespread degeneration and makes firm **localizationist** interpretations difficult, but this is less of a problem with surgical lesions of the cortex
   - several large-scale studies of the language-related deficits experienced by patients with surgical lesions to different areas of the cortex have been conducted; the following are their conclusions:

     1) lesions that destroy Broca's area but little surrounding tissue have **no permanent effect** on language-related abilities (there are temporary problems that develop a few hours after the operation and disappear in several days, which are presumably the result of **edema**);
     2) discrete lesions that cut through the left **arcuate fasciculus** or **angular gyrus** produce **no permanent aphasia;**
     3) because of the dire predictions of the Wernicke-Geschwind model, **Wernicke's area** has rarely been totally removed, but there are some cases in which large portions of it have been removed with **little permanent effect**

   - supporters of the Wernicke-Geschwind model **discount** the data from surgical-lesion studies; they argue that the **cortical organization** of patients requiring neurosurgery is abnormal

   b. **Brain Damage**

   - several independent studies have assessed the degree to which the Wernicke-Geschwind model can account for the effects of **nonsurgical brain damage;** this is exactly the type of evidence on which the model was based
   - the best of these studies have included only cases in which the location of the damage was confirmed by subsequent postmortem examination or visual inspection during surgery
   - for example, a study by Hécaen and Angelergues (1964) assessed the performance on several objective tests of speech production, speech comprehension, and reading performed of 214 right-handed patients whose brain damage was located during a subsequent operation or a postmortem examination
   - they found that: (1) lesions restricted to Broca's area seldom produced lasting deficits, whereas those restricted to Wernicke's area sometimes did not; (2) no case was observed that was purely expressive (Broca's aphasia) or purely receptive (Wernicke's aphasia); and (3) extremely large (involving three lobes) anterior lesions of the left hemisphere tended to produce more expressive symptoms than receptive symptoms, and the opposite was true of very large posterior lesions

   c. **CAT Scans and MRI Scans**

   - since the development of the **CAT** and **MRI,** there have been several efforts to correlate aphasic symptoms with brain scan results
   - brain scans virtually always reveal **extensive cortical** and **subcortical damage** in aphasic patients; aphasia that is **more expressive** than receptive tends to be associated with large **anterior lesions** of the left hemisphere, and aphasia that is **more receptive** than expressive tends to be associated with large **posterior lesions**

- Damasio (1989) used MRI to confirm earlier CT studies, finding that there were large left hemisphere lesions in almost all situations where language-related abilities were eliminated; however, in a few patients' damage was restricted to the **medial frontal lobes** and the **anterior cingulate cortex**, areas not implicated in language according to the Wernicke-Geschwind model.
- Alexander (1989) used CT and MRI to show that aphasia can result from damage to subcortical structures
- Naeser et al., (1982) found aphasia following damage to the **left subcortical white matter**, the left **basal ganglia**, or the left **thalamus**

d.   **Electrical Stimulation**

- in the 1940s, Penfield and his colleagues were the first to **stimulate** the brains of conscious human patients during brain surgery; at some sites the stimulation disrupted various speech-related activities; this suggested that brain stimulation might be a valuable method for **mapping the language areas** of the cortex; stimulation produces a much **more local disruption** than a brain lesion
- in 1959, Penfield and Roberts reported the results obtained from over 10 years of research; they found that: 1) **aphasia-like responses** to right-hemisphere stimulation were **rare;** 2) each deficit was produced by stimulation of sites **scattered** throughout much of the left hemisphere; and 3) there was no apparent tendency for the stimulation of Broca's area to produce deficits different from those produced by stimulation of Wernicke's area
- more recently, Ojemann (1983) assessed naming, reading of simple sentences, short-term verbal memory, ability to mimic orofacial movements, and the ability to recognize **phonemes** (units of sound) during cortical stimulation
- he found that: 1) sites at which stimulation could disrupt language extended **beyond the Wernicke-Geschwind language areas;** 2) all of the specific language abilities were represented in **anterior and posterior sites;** and (3) there were major **differences** across subjects in the **organization** of language abilities
- based on his work, Ojemann has suggested that the language cortex is organized like a mosaic, with the discrete columns of tissue performing a particular function distributed widely throughout the language areas of the cortex

e.   **Current Status of the Wernicke-Geshwind Model**

- research has supported the model's tenets that Broca's area and Wernicke's area are important to language, and that expressive aphasias are generally associated with anterior damage whereas receptive aphasias are more often associated with posterior damage
- little else of the Wernicke-Geschwind model has been supported; however, the model did guide research and clinical diagnosis in the area for almost 30 years…this research led to a new approach to the study of language

4.   **The Cognitive Neuroscience Approach to Language**

- guided by 3 premises:

   Premise 1: that language can be broken down into **constituent cognitive processes** that are much simpler than the cognitive activities that Geschwind (and others) tried to localize to a single part of the brain; these constituent processes include **phonological analysis** (analysis of sounds of language); **grammatical analysis** (analysis of language's structure); and **semantic analysis** (analysis of the meaning of language).

   Premise 2: areas of the brain involved in language are not exclusively involved with that function; for example, areas involved with reading might also be involved with functions like short-term memory or pattern recognition

   Premise 3: the brain areas involved with language are small and widely distributed

- **functional brain imaging techniques** have revolutionized the study of the neural bases of language
- for example, Bavelier and colleagues used a **very sensitive fMRI** to study the activity of the brain during periods of **silent reading;** they found: 1) that only **small areas** are activated at a given time in a single

subject; 2) that these **areas vary** from subject to subject and also within a single subject from trial to trial; 3) that the activity was **spread** over very large areas of the brain; 4) that the active areas were more often in the **left hemisphere** than the right; and 5) that the **activity spread** far beyond those areas predicted by the Wernicke-Geschwind model

- by contrast, Damasio and colleagues used **PET** to study brain activity in the **left temporal lobes** while a person named objects within particular categories; they found that the activated area varied as the category changed, although it was typically somewhere along the anterior-posterior extent of the middle of the left temporal lobe

5. The Cognitive Neuroscience Approach and Dyslexia

- **dyslexia** is an inability to read or write despite normal or superior intelligence; it may be **developmental** or **acquired;** it is a common disorder, affecting about 15% of males and about 5% of females
- there appears to be a genetic component, as it has a heritability estimate of about 0.5; in addition, some neural abnormalities are often present in dyslexics although none have been convincingly linked to the disorder itself
- dyslexia has a cultural component; for example, English speakers are **twice as likely** to be dyslexic as Italian speakers; researchers believe that this is due to the **complexity** of English relative to Italian; PET studies have shown that even though these differences exist, both groups of patients appear to have areas of hypoactivity in the **left posterior temporal lobes** when they are reading
- cognitive researchers have found 2 strategies for reading: a **lexical procedure,** used when material is familiar; and a **phonetic procedure,** used when the words are novel
- these two strategies led to a better understanding of the 2 main types of dyslexia produced by brain damage: **surface dyslexia** occurs when patients lose their lexical skills, whereas **deep dyslexia** occurs when patients lose their phonetic reading skills
- interestingly, deep dyslexics most often have damage to the left hemisphere language areas…suggesting that the phonetic skills are distributed widely over the frontal and temporal lobes of the left hemisphere

Suggested Websites for Lecture 16b:

Dyslexia: *http://www.sciam.com/1196issue/1196shaywitz.html*
    From Scientific American, a review of the neural bases of dyslexia

Conversation's With Neil's Brain: *http://williamcalvin.com/bk7/bk7.htm*
    A full-text version of the book by William Calvin and George Ojemann; very well-written exposition on language and laterality of function, amongst other topics…an easy read, but fun and interesting.

Neural Bases of Dyslexia: http://www.sfn.org/content/Publications/BrainBriefings/dyslexia.html
    A brief overview from the Society for Neuroscience.

Language and the Brain:
        http://www.med.harvard.edu/publications/On_The_Brain/Volume4/Number4/F95Lang.html
    From Harvard's Mahoney Institute, a very readable article on language and the brain.

Evolution and Language: *http://www.brainconnection.com/topics/?main=fa/evolution-language*
    An interesting piece from the Brain Connection website.

Language Learning Impairments: *http://www.newhorizons.org/blab_tallal1.html*
    A very interesting article on novel strategies for language remediation, by Dr. Paula Tallal and the Brain Lab.

IM-AT-A-GLANCE: Chapter 17. Biopsychology of Emotion, Stress & Health
Fear, the Dark Side of Emotion

Detailed Outline	Print Supplements	Media Supplements	Professor's Notes
Chapter 17. Biopsychology of Emotion, Stress & Health: Fear, the Dark Side of Emotion pp. 437-460 17.1 Biopsychology of Emotion: Introduction 17.2 Fear, Defense and Aggression 17.3 Stress and Health 17.4 Fear Conditioning 17.5 Brain Mechanisms of Human Emotion	**Instructor's Manual for** *BIOPSYCHOLOGY,* *Lecture 17a, Lecture 17b, and Lecture 17c* **Test Bank for** *BIOPSYCHOLOGY,* *Chapter 17* **Study Guide for** *BIOPSYCHOLOGY,* *Chapter 17* **Transparencies for Physiological Psychology:** *X. Emotion* *XIV. Stress & Mental Illness;* use TR141 –TR143	**Beyond the Brain & Behavior CD for** *BIOPSYCHOLOGY:* *Practice Tests for Chapter 17* *Hard Copy for Chapter 17* *Electronic Flashcards for Chapter 17* **Digital Image Archive, PowerPoint Presentation and Bitmap Images for** *BIOPSYCHOLOGY:* *Chapter 17*	

Lecture 17a

BIOPSYCHOLOGY OF EMOTION

Outline

1. Early Research on the Biopsychology of Emotion
   a. Darwin
   b. James-Lange and Cannon-Bard Theories
   c. Sham Rage, the Limbic System, and Kulver-Bucy Syndrome

2. Emotions and the Autonomic Nervous System

3. Human Facial Expressions of Emotion
   a. The Primary Facial Expressions
   b. Facial Feedback Hypothesis
   c. Deceptive Facial Expressions

Lecture Notes

1. **Early Research on the Biopsychology of Emotion** (see Fig. 17.1 - Fig.17.4 in *BIOPSYCHOLOGY;* use *Digital Image Archive Figure CH17F01.BMP*, *CH17F02.BMP* and *CH17F03.BMP)*

a. Darwin

- Darwin's **The Expression of Emotions in Man and Animals** was the first major event in the study of the biopsychological bases of emotion
- Darwin believed that **emotions evolved** from behaviors that indicated what an animal would do next in a given situation; that when these behaviors were **advantageous** to the animal (e.g., allowed it to avoid a fight), they evolved in a way that would **enhance their communicative value,** to the extent that the original behavior was lost; and that **opposite messages** are signaled by opposite types of behaviors (**the principle of antithesis**)

b. James-Lange and Cannon-Bard Theories of Emotion

- the **James-Lange theory** was the first attempt to explain the **physiological bases of emotion;** in their theory, James and Lange suggested that **emotion-inducing stimuli** are received and interpreted by the brain, which triggers **visceral changes** that subsequently trigger the **experience of emotion.**
- Cannon, and subsequently Bard, proposed an alternative theory based on the idea that **emotional stimuli** evoke **visceral** and an **emotional responses** that are **independent** of one another
- it appears that neither theory was entirely correct; emotions can be induced by stimuli that cannot elicit a peripheral, visceral response (e.g., in patients suffering from a spinal cord transection), but visceral responses can often induce an emotional state in the absence of any obvious eliciting stimuli (e.g., a racing heartbeat and increased respiration can produce a feeling of fear in the absence of an eliciting stimuli)
- more recently, a third theory has been reached that suggests that each of the **3 factors** in an emotional response—the **perception** of the emotion-inducing stimulus, the **autonomic and somatic responses** to the stimulus, and the **experience of emotion**—influence the other 2 factors

c. **Sham Rage, the Limbic System, and the Kulver-Bucy Syndrome**

- in 1929, Bard reported that **decorticate cats** responded with unusual **aggression** to the slightest provocation; often, this behavior was **not directed** at any specific topic. Bard concluded that the **hypothalamus** is critical for the performance of these aggressive behaviors, which he called **sham rage;** he also believed that the cortex normally **inhibited** and **directed** these aggressive displays.
- this theory of hypothalamic function was followed by Papez's proposal of a **limbic system** that controlled the expression of emotions by connections with the hypothalamus and mediated the perception of emotions by connections with the cortex
- this idea was supported in part by the observation that damage to the amygdala (a part of the limbic system) would produce a syndrome in which a subject was fearless, hypersexual, and inclined to explore objects with their mouths. This was called the **Kluver-Bucy syndrome,** after the investigators who first reported it

2. **Emotions and the Autonomic Nervous System**

- a large body of research in the area has focused on the degree to which **specific patterns** of ANS activity are associated with **specific emotions;** the results suggest that both the James-Lange theory (which predicts a multitude of activity patterns, each generating a unique emotion) and the Canon-Bard theory (which predicts a single general pattern of activation) are partially correct
- in addition, the **effectiveness of ANS** measures in **polygraphy** has been extensively studied; these tests examine changes in emotions, as indexed by ANS activity, to assess the truthfulness of a person's claims
- many of these studies employ a **control-question technique** in which a person's answers to innocuous questions to which the answers are known (Is your mother's name Kerin?) are compared to answers to the target question of interest (Did you steal the purse?).
- in many cases, any normal person will react strongly to the target question and make it difficult to for an investigator to determine whether or not they are lying; to circumvent this possibility, Lykken (1959) developed the **guilty-knowledge technique** in which the polygrapher asks a series of questions that contain possible details about the crime
- only some of these details are actually true, however; the polygrapher compares a subject's responses to "true" details (that only a guilty suspect could know) to their responses to "false" details (that would make innocent parties equally uneasy) to determine if someone is not telling the truth

3. **Human Facial Expressions of Emotion** (see Fig. 17.5 - Fig.17.7 in *BIOPSYCHOLOGY;* use *Digital Image Archive Figure CH17F08.BMP)*

a. **The Primary Facial Expressions**

- much of the classic research on human facial expressions has been conducted by **Ekman** and **Friesen**
- beginning in the 1970s; they began by analyzing hundreds of films and photographs of people experiencing various emotions; they concluded that there are **six primary facial expressions of emotion** and that all other expressions were mixtures of these; the six primary expressions were expressions of: (1) **anger,** (2) **fear,** (3) **happiness,** (4) **surprise,** (5) **sadness,** and (6) **disgust**
- **Darwin** had earlier proposed that **facial expressions are universal** to the human species; this hypothesis was tested by showing people from 12 different cultures pictures of different facial expressions
- the photographs were of people who had been instructed to contract specific facial muscles (e.g., to make a surprised expression, the models were instructed to pull their eyebrows upward so as to wrinkle their forehead, to open their eyes wide to reveal white above the iris, to slacken the muscles around the mouth, and to drop the jaw)
- the people from **all 12 cultures linked the same emotions to the facial expressions**, thus supporting Darwin's hypothesis. In addition, Ekman and Friesen found that isolated New Guinea tribe members could correctly identify Western facial expressions and that Westerners could correctly identify New Guinean expressions, further supporting the idea of the universality of emotions

b.   Facial Feedback Hypothesis of Emotions

- recall that, according to the James-Lange theory of emotion, the body first produces a **visceral, peripheral response** to emotional stimuli, and then the feeling of **emotion** comes from the body's perception of its own reactions; although it is now clear that feedback from the body's reactions is not necessary to feel emotion, the question remains, "Can the expression of emotion influence the feeling of emotion?"
- one version of this hypothesis focuses on the idea that facial expression can influence emotional experience. This is called the **facial feedback hypothesis**: Can putting on a happy face make you feel better?
- the answer seems to be yes; Rutledge and Hupka (1985) asked subjects to hold various facial poses while they viewed slides; the subjects reported being slightly more happy when making happy faces, and slightly more angry when making angry faces

c.   Deceptive Facial Expressions

- because we can exert voluntary control over the facial muscles, we can inhibit true facial expressions and substitute false ones
- it is difficult to fool an expert because **microexpressions** of the genuine emotion often break through the false one; although they are usually very short (about .05 seconds), they can often be spotted by an expert even without slow-motion analysis
- also, there tend to be subtle differences between genuine and false expressions that can be recognized by an expert; for example, **Duchenne** a French neuroanatomist pointed out in 1862 that genuine smiles (which have been known as **Duchenne smiles**) involve contraction of both the **zygomaticus major** and **orbicularis oculi**, whereas false smiles involve only the zygomaticus major
- **EMG recordings** can detect emotional changes even when the motor output to the facial muscles is too slight to change them
- Dimberg and colleagues have found that observers often unconsciously mimic the expressions of the person that they are watching

Suggested Websites for Lecture 17a:

The Laughing Brain: *http://faculty.washington.edu/chudler/laugh.html*
   From Dr. Chulder's most excellent website, a look at the neural bases of laughter.

The Limbic System: *http://www.epub.org.br/cm/n05/mente/limbic_i.htm*
   From the Brain and Mind site, a review of the limbic system and its role in emotion.

Lecture 17b

STRESS AND HEALTH

Outline

1. The Stress Response

2. Stress and Ulcers

3. Psychoneuroimmunology: Stress and Infection

4. Stress and the Hippocampus

Lecture Notes

1. **The Stress Response** (see Fig. 17.8 in *BIOPSYCHOLOGY;* use *Digital Image Archive Figure CH17F10.BMP*)

- **Selye** first described the stress response in the 1950's; he identified several physiological responses to stress, emphasizing the role of the **anterior pituitary-adrenal cortex system** and the effects of stress on the release of ACTH, and glucocorticoids.
- Selye also recognized the **dual nature** of stress: **acute stress** elicited adaptive changes that allowed an organism to cope with the stressor, but **chronic stress** produced changes that were maladaptive
- recent research has also implicated the importance of the sympathetic nervous system's release of **epinephrine** and **norepinephrine** in the response to stress
- McEwen (1994) hypothesized that the magnitude of the stress response was dependent upon 3 factors: the **stressor**, the **individual**, and **strategies to cope** with stress
- Selye's work remains important to the psychological sciences because it provided a link through which psychological factors might impact upon physical illness. **Psychosomatic illnesses** are ones that have a physical basis that is greatly influenced by psychological factors. Two examples of psychosomatic illness include **ulcers** and **infection.**

2. **Stress and Ulcers** (see Fig. 17.9 and Fig.17.10 in *BIOPSYCHOLOGY)*

- **gastric ulcers** are painful lesions to the lining of the stomach and small intestine; stress has been implicated in their development, with the key factor being a stress-induced increase in acidic gastric secretions accompanied by decreased blood flow through the wall of the stomach.
- research had suggested that the bacteria *Helicobacter pylori* are responsible for all ulcers except by those caused by nonsteroidal anti-inflammatory drugs.
- however, it seems as though *H. pylori* by itself is not sufficient to induce the formation of ulcers, as it is found in about 75% of all control subjects, too. Currently, researchers believe that stress-induced increases in gastric secretions and decreases in blood flow interact with *H. pylori* to produce ulcers.

3. **Psychoneuroimmunology: Stress and Infection**

- **psychoneuroimmunology is** the study of interactions among psychological, nervous system, and immune system responses allows a theoretical basis for studying a person's resistance to disease and infection
- the **immune system** puts up barriers to keep the body from being taken over by invading microorganisms
- **phagocytosis** is a nonspecific mechanism by which foreign microorganisms are destroyed; this process is carried out by **macrophages**

- there is also a second, more specific mechanism for dealing with foreign microorganisms and debris
- **antigens** are protein molecules on a cell's surface that identify it as foreign or native
- **lymphocytes** are specialized white blood cells, produced in the bone marrow, and stored in the lymphatic system; there are two types of lymphocytes, that each mediate a form of immunological defense:

   i) **T cells** are lymphocytes that destroy invading microorganisms in a process called **cell-mediated immunity**; when a foreign micro-organism is detected by a **macrophage,** the macrophage displays the foreign organisms **antigens**; T-cells with the appropriate receptors are attracted to the antigens, multiply to create more T-cells, which destroy the micro-organisms

   ii) **B cells** are lymphocytes that manufacture **antibodies** (lethal receptor molecules) against antigens encountered on foreign cells and debris, in a process called **antibody-mediated immunity**; B-cells bind to foreign cells and produce **antibodies** which are released into the extracellular fluid to destroy the foreign micro-organism

- in humans, stress from sources such as final examinations, sleep deprivation, divorce, bereavement etc., has been shown to **decrease the effectiveness of the immune system.** Unfortunately, these results are not straightforward to interpret as there are many possible **confounds**; for example, stressed subjects may report more illnesses because they expect to be ill, the experience of illness may be worse under stress, or stress may cause illness-inducing behavioral changes rather than the illness itself (e.g., decreases in sleep; alterations in diet)
- in support of these human findings, similar results have been seen in laboratory animals exposed to electric shocks, social defeat, overcrowding etc. Together, these **converging lines of data** suggest that stress may play a major role in our susceptibility to many infectious diseases.
- stress may affect the immune system by affecting **hormonal activity** mediated through the **anterior pituitary-adrenal cortex system** and the **sympathetic adrenal medulla system;** for example, both T-cells and B-cells have receptors for **glucocorticoids** and for **norepinephrine** and **epinephrine**, which are all released in very high levels during periods of stress
- **early experience** may play a key role in determining how animals will deal with stress as adults; for example, rat pups that are groomed the most by their mothers are less responsive to stress as adults

4. Stress and the Hippocampus

- the **hippocampus** is particularly rich in **glucocorticoid receptors,** a fact that makes the hippocampus particularly sensitive to the effects of stress; just a few **hours** of stress in lab animals can change the hippocampus for months
- these changes include **shrinking of dendrites** of hippocampal neurons and reduced **neurogenesis** in the hippocampus after a stressful experience
- **four important points** about the effects of stress on the hippocampus have emerged:

   i) the effects can have **behavioral consequences;** for example, stressed rats are impaired on behavioral tasks that require the integrity of the hippocampus;
   ii) the protective effects of **maternal care** extend into the **old age** of a rat; rats that received the most care as pups showed the least amount of hippocampal dysfunction and less hippocampal cell loss as adults;
   iii) **natural stressors** produce **more hippocampal pathology** than experimental ones;
   iv) **females** develop **less stress-related pathology** in their hippocampi; this may be due to the neuroprotective effects of **estradiol**

Suggested Websites for Chapter 17b:

Stress and Pychosomatic Disorders: *http://www.epub.org.br/cm/n03/doencas/stress_i.htm*
A look at stress and its effects on general health, from the Brain and Mind site.

Stress and the Developing Brain: *http://www.nimh.nih.gov/publicat/develop.cfm*
From the NIH, a good overview of the effects of stress on brain development.

Lecture 17c

FEAR AND HUMAN EMOTIONS

Outline

1. Fear, Defense and Aggression

2. Fear Conditioning
    a. The Amygdala and Fear Conditioning
    b. The Hippocampus and Contextual Fear Conditioning

3. Brain Mechanisms of Human Emotion
    a. Specific Brain Regions Have Specific Roles
    b. The Right Hemisphere is More Involved in Human Emotion
    c. Individual Differences in the Neural Substrates of Emotion

Lecture Notes

1. Fear, Defense and Aggression

-   **fear** is the emotional reaction to threat; **defensive behaviors** are intended to protect an animal from threat, while **aggressive behaviors** are intended to threaten or harm.
-   **ethoexperimental research** on emotional expression in nonhuman species has focused on aggression and defense, primarily in rats
-   **two important concepts** have emerged from this study:

    i) neither aggression or defense are unitary concepts; there are different kinds of aggression and defense, which occur in **different situations**, have a **different topography**, and have a **different neural basis**;
    ii) many of the complexities of aggressive and defensive behavior can be understood in terms of the concept of **target sites**, the idea that different kinds of aggression tend to be directed at particular sites on the defender's body and that various defensive maneuvers appear to be specifically designed to protect these sites

    -   recognition of different types of aggression and defense, and the **stereotypical nature** of many of the behaviors associated with them, have helped researchers studying the neural bases of these behaviors
    -   for example, lesioning the **septal nuclei** in a rat produces a state commonly referred to as **septal rage**, in which the rat is very hard to handle. This lesion was believed to increase the aggressiveness of the rat…but closer analyses revealed that the septal lesions actually made the rat **more defensive.**

    -   perhaps of more interest is the fact that such analyses have solved a long-standing mystery: Why does **testosterone enhance aggression** in nonhuman species, but not in humans? One explanation is that human aggression is under **different neural and humeral control.**

    -   however, Albert and his colleagues have suggested that most human "aggression" is actually a response to a **perceived threat**…and therefore should be considered a **defensive behavior**, which is NOT affected by testosterone levels in nonhuman species, either

2. **Fear Conditioning** (see Fig. 17.11 in *BIOPSYCHOLOGY*; use *Digital Image Archive Figure CH17F09.BMP)*

- **fear conditioning** is the establishment of fear in response to a previously neutral stimulus like a **tone** (the CS+) by pairing it with the presentation of an aversive stimulus like a **footshock** (the US)
- LeDoux and his colleagues have mapped the neural substrates for this form of **auditory fear conditioning**

a. **The Amygdala and Fear Conditioning**

- LeDoux found that lesions to the **medial geniculate nucleus** of the thalamus blocked fear conditioning, but lesions to **primary auditory cortex** did not.
- this suggested that the medial geniculate nucleus projected to an alternate neural structure that was involved in the fear conditioning; this turned out to be the **amygdala,** as lesions there also blocked the auditory fear conditioning.
- pathways from the amygdala to the **periaqueductal gray** mediate many **defensive behaviors;** pathways to the **lateral hypothalamus** elicit the appropriate **sympathetic responses.**
- interestingly, there is a **second pathway** from the **medial geniculate** nucleus of the thalamus to the **amygdala** that passes through **primary auditory cortex;** if either the direct or the indirect route is intact, fear conditioning can occur.

b. **The Hippocampus and Contextual Fear Conditioning**

- the **context** or environment in which fear-inducing stimuli are encountered can also come to elicit fear; this is called **contextual fear conditioning**
- given the role of the hippocampus in **spatial memory,** it is not surprising that this brain structure is also involved in contextual fear conditioning; lesioning the hippocampus blocks the development of contextual fear conditioning *without blocking conditioning to a CS+*, and lesioning the hippocampus just after conditioning has taken place blocks the retention of the contextual fear conditioning without blocking retention of the fear response to an explicit CS+

3. **Brain Mechanisms of Human Emotion** (see Fig. 17.12 in *BIOPSYCHOLOGY;* use *Digital Image Archive Figure CH17F09.BMP)*

a. **Specific Brain Regions Have Specific Roles**

- this research has focused on neuropsychological studies of brain-damaged patients, and functional imaging studies in health subjects
- in general, these studies have confirmed a role for the **amygdala** and **prefrontal cortex** in human emotion…and failed to support the limbic theory of emotion
- researchers have found that brain regions involved with one emotion are not necessarily involved in another…and that a brain region might be involved in one aspect of an emotion but not another aspect of the same emotion
- for example, the amygdala appears to be very involved in the **perception** (as opposed to the **expression)** of fear…lesioning the amygdala leaves a person or animal unable to perceive fearful emotions in others, although these patients have no problems matching the appropriate emotion with a particular sentence or in expressing various emotions using facial expression upon request

- a similar deficit is seen in patients with **Urback-Wiethe disease,** in which the tissue forming the amygdala and medial temporal lobes is **calcified** and destroyed
- furthermore, fMRI has revealed that the **lateral aspects** of the **frontal lobes** are most associated with **positive emotions,** whereas the **medial aspects** of the **frontal lobes** are most associated with **negative emotions**

b. The Right Hemisphere is More Involved in Human Emotion

- studies involving brain damaged patients and functional imaging techniques have both revealed that, in general, the **right hemisphere** tends to play a **greater role** in emotional behaviors; however, this depends on the structure under consideration and the particular aspect of emotion under study
- for example, the **right hemisphere** in general is more involved in the perception of emotion, both in terms of **facial expression** and **prosody**
- upon closer analysis, however, it was noted that lesions of the right or left frontal lobes **equally disrupt** perception of emotion from facial features, whereas lesions of the right, but not the left, temporal lobe disrupt it
- by contrast, PET studies indicated that the right amygdala and prefrontal cortex are **more active in prosody,** whereas the right temporal lobe is less responsive than the left
- the dominance of the right hemisphere in emotional behaviors is also revealed by analyzing emotional expression themselves; facial expression appear sooner, and are of greater magnitude, on the left side of the face…the side controlled by the right hemisphere

c. Individual differences in the Neural Substrates of Emotion

- unlike motor and sensory areas of the brain, there is considerable variability in the neural substrates of emotion.
- for example, some patients with bilateral amygdalar damage completely lose their ability to perceive emotions related to fear; some lose their ability to perceive other emotions; and some suffer from no apparent dysfunction at all!
- fMRI has revealed that people with different personalities also have brains that react differently to emotional stimuli…people who tend to be positive react most strongly to pleasant images, whereas people who tend to be negative react most strongly to unpleasant images

Suggested Websites for Chapter 17c:

Neural Bases of Fear: *http://thalamus.wustl.edu/course/limbic.html*
>Fear and the limbic system, from Washington University's Neuroscience tutorial page. You will have to scroll down the page to find this section; brief text, good figures. In addition, check out: *http://www.the-scientist.com/yr1998/june/research_980622.html*

Imaging the Emotional Brain: *http://www.news.wisc.edu/packages/emotion/index.msql?get=media*
>From the University of Wisconsin's *Science of Emotions* site (you should really check out the whole thing); go to the bottom of this page for some great movies of how different patterns of brain activity underlie different emotional states.

The Laughing Brain: *http://apu.sfn.org/content/Publications/BrainBriefings/bb_humor.htm*
>A look at the brain regions activated when we are happy, from the Society for Neuroscience's website.

IM-AT-A-GLANCE: Chapter 18. Biopsychology of Psychiatric Disorders: The Brain Unhinged

Detailed Outline	Print Supplements	Media Supplements	Professor's Notes
Chapter 18. Biopsychology of Psychiatric Disorders: The Brain Unhinged, pp. 461-480 18.1 Schizophrenia 18.2 Affective Disorders: Depression and Mania 18.3 Anxiety Disorders 18.4 Tourette's Syndrome 18.5 Clinical Trials: Development of New Psychotherapeutic Drugs	**Instructor's Manual for** *BIOPSYCHOLOGY,* *Lecture 18a and Lecture 18b* **Test Bank for** *BIOPSYCHOLOGY,* *Chapter 18* **Study Guide for** *BIOPSYCHOLOGY,* *Chapter 18* **Transparencies for Physiological Psychology:** *XIV. Stress & Mental Illness,* Use TR144-146	**Beyond the Brain & Behavior CD for** *BIOPSYCHOLOGY:* *Practice Tests for Chapter 18* *Hard Copy for Chapter 18* *Electronic Flashcards for Chapter 18* **Digital Image Archive, PowerPoint Presentation and Bitmap Images for** *BIOPSYCHOLOGY:* *Chapter 17*	

Lecture 18a

SCHIZOPHRENIA and AFFECTIVE DISORDERS

Outline

1. Schizophrenia
   a) Symptoms and Etiology
   b) The First Antischizophrenic Drugs
   c) Dopamine Theory of Schizophrenia
   d) The Dopamine Theory: Unanswered Questions

2. Affective Disorders
   a) Symptoms and Etiology
   b) Antidepressant Drugs
   c) Monoamine Theory of Depression
   d) Diathesis-Stress Model of Depression

Lecture Notes

- a **psychiatric disorder** is a psychological disorder that is severe enough that is requires treatment by a clinical psychologist or a psychiatrist
- traditionally, psychological disorders have been viewed as being either **psychiatric** or **neuropsychological;** this dichotomy reflects the archaic view that mind is something other than a brain function **(mind-brain debate)** and the distinction between these 2 views of psychological disorders has blurred
- nonetheless, there are still some differences between neuropsychological disorders and psychiatric disorders…the latter tend to be less well understood, involve more **subtle pathology,** and be influenced more by **experiential factors** like stress

1. **Schizophrenia** (see Fig. 18.1 and Fig. 18.2 in *BIOPSYCHOLOGY;* use *Digital Image Archive Figure CH17F14.BMP)*

   a) Symptoms and Etiology

   - **schizophrenia** literally means a splitting of psychic function ("the shattered mind"); it is characterized by a complex and diverse set of symptoms that often overlap with other forms of mental illness and may change with time
   - individuals with any of the following symptoms are diagnosed as schizophrenic: **bizarre delusions, hallucinations, inappropriate affect, incoherent thought,** or **odd behavior** (e.g., **catatonia)**
   - about 1% of the population is schizophrenic; the incidence appears to be about the same in all parts of the world
   - a **genetic basis** for the disease emerged when it was recognized that the concordance rate of schizophrenia in identical twins is about 45%; in fraternal twins or sibs it is about 10%
   - regions of **several different chromosomes** have been implicated in the vulnerability to schizophrenia
   - in addition to a genetic predisposition, experiences such as **prenatal trauma, infection,** and **stress** may all be susceptibility factors
   - clearly schizophrenia is influenced by both genetics and experience; the current view is that people inherit a **predisposition** for schizophrenia which may or may not be activated **by experience**

b) The First Antischizophrenic Drugs

- **chlorpromazine** was initially developed by a drug company as a new **antihistamine**; in the early 1950s a French physician used the drug to prevent the swelling associated with surgery; by chance he noticed that chlorpromazine also seemed to calm his patients down
- the physician recommended that chlorpromazine be used as a **sedative** in difficult-to-manage psychiatric cases; in most cases it didn't seem to work; however, one psychiatrist noticed a marked improvement in several **schizophrenic** patients after 3 weeks
- amazingly chlorpromazine seemed to calm agitated schizophrenic patients and to activate catatonic ones; therefore the effect seemed **specifically antischizophrenic**, not just **sedative** (sleep-inducing)
- at the same time, an American psychiatrist became interested in reports that the **snake root plant** had been used for centuries in India as a cure for various psychiatric disturbances
- **reserpine**, the active ingredient of the snakeroot plant, had been isolated so he gave it to some of his schizophrenic patients
- it proved to be an effective antischizophrenic; however, it is no longer used for treatment of schizophrenia due to its effects of dangerously lowering blood pressure

c) Dopamine Theory of Schizophrenia

- given the dissimilarity of the structure of chlorpromazine and reserpine, the **similarity of their effects** was remarkable; their therapeutic effects did not occur until **2 or 3 weeks** after the beginning of therapy, and at that time both drugs started to produce **side effects;** mild **tremors** at rest, **muscular rigidity,** and a **decrease in voluntary movement**
- you should recognize these as the symptoms of **Parkinson's disease**; it seemed that the neurochemical changes that were the basis of these drugs' antischizophrenic action were related to pathology that underlies Parkinson's symptoms
- in 1960, it was discovered that there was a deficiency of **dopamine** in the brains of Parkinson's patients; thus it seemed that both chlorpromazine and reserpine reduced brain dopamine levels and that this reduction was alleviating the symptoms of schizophrenia; on the basis of these two inferences it was proposed that schizophrenia is associated with **excessive activity in dopaminergic systems** in the brain
- two previous findings lent support to this **dopamine theory of schizophrenia:**

  i) reserpine was known to be a **dopamine antagonist** (it depleted the brain of dopamine and other monoamines by causing them to leak from their vesicles); and
  ii) **stimulants**, which are agonists of dopamine and other monoamines, trigger schizophrenic episodes in healthy subjects at high doses (e.g., **amphetamine psychosis**)

- in 1963, **Carlsson** and **Lindqvist** tested the dopamine theory; they expected to show that chlorpromazine, like reserpine, depletes the brain of dopamine--but they didn't; instead, they found that chlorpromazine left dopamine levels unchanged, but that it produced a great **increase in dopamine metabolites**
- they concluded that, like reserpine, chlorpromazine is a **dopamine antagonist**, but that it antagonizes dopamine in a different way
- they suggested that chlorpromazine is a **false transmitter** at dopamine synapses; that a **feedback signal** produced by the inactivity of the postsynaptic neurons causes the presynaptic neurons to **release more dopamine;** that this excess of dopamine is immediately broken down by enzymes in the synapse because all of the binding sites are taken up by chlorpromazine; and that as a result dopamine levels stay about the same but metabolite levels increase
- a technique developed in the mid 1970s allowed Snyder and his colleagues to measure the degree to which various antischizophrenic drugs bind to dopamine receptors, and to relate this **binding affinity** to the potency with which each drug alleviated schizophrenic symptoms in human patients
- the correlation was positive, but there were some disturbing exceptions; for example, **haloperidol**, one of the most potent antischizophrenic drugs, bound only weakly to dopamine receptors
- the answer to this puzzle was suggested by the discovery that there is more than one type of **dopamine receptor**; to date, a total of five dopamine receptors have been identified D_1 and D_2
- it turned out that chlorpromazine and all other antischizophrenic drugs of the same chemical class (i.e., the **phenothiazines**) bind with equal affinity to both D_1 and D_2 receptors; in contrast, haloperidol and the other **butyrophenones** bind with highest affinity to D_2 receptors

- this suggested a modification to the dopamine theory of schizophrenia, as schizophrenia could now be viewed as being caused by excess activity at D_2 receptors and alleviated by drugs that block activity at D_2 receptors

d) The Dopamine Theory of Schizophrenia: Unanswered Questions

- there are four questions about the dopamine theory of schizophrenia that have yet to be resolved:

i) Are D_2 receptors the only ones involved in schizophrenia?

- the effectiveness of **clozapine**, an atypical neuroleptic that binds poorly to D_2 receptors, suggests that this may not be so. Clozapine and conventional neuroleptics bind to **D_1 and D_4 receptors** and some **serotonin** receptors; perhaps these may also be involved in schizophrenia.
- however, all atypical neuroleptics DO bind somewhat to D_2 receptors…and recent evidence suggests that newly diagnosed schizophrenics, who have not yet been medicated, have elevated numbers of D_2 receptors in their brains.

ii) Why does it take several weeks for neuroleptics to work?

- it appears that the therapeutic effect of blockade is mediated by **neural adaptation** (slow developing compensatory changes) to the blockade of dopamine receptors, rather than by the blockade itself
- one hypothesis is that prolonged neuroleptic treatment eventually produces **depolarization blockade** in dopamine neurons, and it is this decrease in activity that is related to the drug's therapeutic effect.

iii) What parts of the brain are involved in schizophrenia?

- imaging studies have revealed many changes, including **small cerebral cortices** and **large ventricles.** The cortical abnormalities are most prevalent in the **prefrontal, cingulate** and **temporal cortices;** surprisingly, little pathology in brain dopaminergic systems has been reported.
- there is some evidence that schizophrenia is a **neurodevelopmental disorder;** there is no obvious ongoing degeneration in the brain of schizophrenic patients, and the pathology observed is largely developed by the time diagnosis is first made

iv) Why are neuroleptics effective against only some of the symptoms of schizophrenia?

- the current hypothesis is that cases dominated by **positive symptoms** (hallucinations, delusions, incoherence) are caused by excess D_2 activity and are helped; cases dominated by **negative symptoms** (catatonia, blunt affect, poverty of speech) are attributable to brain damage and are not helped.

2. **Affective Disorders** (see Fig. 18.3 in *BIOPSYCHOLOGY;* use *Digital Image Archive Figure CH17F15.BMP)*

    a) Symptoms and Etiology

    -   all of us have experienced depression; people in whom depression is so severe and so frequent, often without obvious cause, are said to be suffering from the psychiatric disorder of **depression**
    -   depression is characterized by intense feelings of **despair, hypoactivity, sleep problems, withdrawal, lack of appetite,** and an **inability to care for oneself**
    -   **mania** is the other type of affective disorder; in many respects it is the opposite of depression as patients with mania are overconfident, impulsive, distractible and highly energetic
    -   many people who suffer from depression also suffer from mania; these people are said to suffer from a **bipolar affective illness;** people who simply suffer from depression are said to suffer from a **unipolar affective illness**
    -   depression can be **reactive** (triggered by negative experiences) or **endogenous,** (no apparent external triggers)
    -   about **6%** of people suffer from unipolar affective disorder and **1%** from bipolar affective disorder at some point in their lives; about **10%** of people suffering from an affective disorder will commit **suicide**
    -   the **concordance rate** for bipolar affective disorder for identical twins is about 60%; for fraternal twins it is about 15%; thus, there is a strong genetic component
    -   like schizophrenia, **stress** plays a major role in the etiology of affective disorders; stress can trigger attacks of depression, and there is some indication that early exposure to stress increases the likelihood of developing depression in adulthood

    b) Antidepressant Drugs

    -   the first antidepressant drug, **iproniazid,** was developed as a treatment for tuberculosis; it had no effect on tuberculosis, but it did leave the patients less depressed about their condition and its clinical usefulness in this regard was soon exploited
    -   iproniazid is an **monoamine oxidase (MAO) inhibitor;** MAO inhibitors in combination with **tyramine-rich** foods (e.g., cheese, wine, or pickles) cause **life-threatening** surges in blood pressure; this is called the **cheese effect**
    -   **imipramine,** the first **tricyclic antidepressant,** was initially developed as an antischizophrenic drug; when it was tried on a mixed group of psychiatric patients, it was found to be ineffective against schizophrenia but affective against depression; tricyclic antidepressants block the reuptake of both **serotonin** and **norepinephrine** and are safer than MAO inhibitors
    -   **lithium** is affective against mania as well as depression; it was discovered when an Australian psychiatrist, John Cade, attempted to induce experimental mania in guinea pigs by injecting the urine of manic patients, mixed with lithium chloride to form an injectable salt
    -   the guinea pigs became very inactive, even those in the lithium-chloride control group; thus, he concluded that lithium had **calmed** the guinea pigs
    -   in fact, the lithium had merely made the guinea pigs **ill;** nevertheless, this study encouraged some clinical trials and it was found to be effective against mania (and sometimes depression) in bipolar patients
    -   lithium's therapeutic effects are believed to be due to its agonistic action on **serotonin function;** lithium is still widely used in the treatment of mania but is being replaced as a treatment for bipolar affective disorders by drugs that are more affective against depression
    -   **selective serotonin reuptake inhibitors (SSRIs), such as Prozac,** are a variation of tricyclic antidepressants which selectively block serotonin uptake.
    -   SSRI's are not more effective than imipramine and other tricyclics against depression but they have fewer side effects and have they are effective against many types of psychological disorders
    -   recently, **selective norepinephrine reuptake inhibitors (SNRIs)** have proven equal effective in the treatment of depression

c) Monoamine Theory of Depression

- the most widely accepted theory of depression
- based on the fact that all clinically effective tricyclic antidepressants are **serotonin** and/or **norepinephrine agonists;** thus, it depression may be due to **underactivity** at serotonin and norepinephrine synapses
- in support of this theory, there is evidence that certain norepinephrine and serotonin receptors are elevated in untreated depressed patients; this may be due to low levels of transmitters eliciting a compensatory increase in receptors called **receptor up-regulation**
- however, this theory cannot explain why antidepressants take **3 or more weeks** to take effect although they immediately increase extracellular monoamine levels or why serotonin and norepinephrine agonists are **equally effective**

d) Diathesis-Stress Theory of Depression

- this theory is based on the idea that some people inherit a **diathesis** (genetic predisposition) for depression; if the individual is stressed early in life their systems become altered so that they are hypersensitive to stress for the rest of their lives. This leads to the development of depression.
- this is based on the observation that depressed patients synthesize more **corticotrophin-releasing hormone** from their hypothalamus, which causes a greater release of **adrenocorticotropic hormone** from the anterior pituitary, which caused increased **glucocorticoid** release from the adrenal cortex.

Suggested Websites for Lecture 18a:

Neural Bases of Depression: *http://www.sciam.com/1998/0698issue/0698nemeroff.html*
> From Scientific American, an article by Dr. Charles Nemeroff on the neural bases of depression; includes information about norepinephrine, serotonin, corticotrophin-releasing hormone and the contribution of new imaging techniques in the study of depression.

Shock Therapy: *http://www.epub.org.br/cm/n04/historia/shock_i.htm*
> From the Brain and Mind site and the State University of Campinas in Brazil, an examination of the role of ECT, insulin shock, convulsions and other forms of "shock therapy"; interesting historical overview of a controversial topic.

The Discovery of Antipsychotics: *http://www.pbs.org/wgbh/aso/databank/entries/dh52dr.html*
> From the Public Broadcasting System's A Science Odyssey, a description of Laborit's discovery of chlopromazine.

Schizophrenia Information: *http://www.schizophrenia.com/*
> A great source of information about schizophrenia; many links to other sites

National Alliance for Research on Schizophrenia and Depression: *http://www.mhsource.com/narsad/*
> Support fore research into major mental illness.

Lecture 18b

ANXIETY DISORDERS, TOURETTE'S SYNDROME, and DEVELOPING NEW PSYCHOTHERAPEUTIC DRUGS

Outline

1. Anxiety Disorders
   a. Symptoms and Classification
   b. Pharmacological Treatment of Anxiety Disorders
   c. Neural Bases of Anxiety Disorders

2. Tourette's Syndrome
   a. Symptoms and Etiology
   b. Brain Mechanisms and Treatment

3. Development of New Psychotherapeutic Drugs

Lecture Notes

1. Anxiety Disorders

a. Symptoms and Classification

- **Anxiety** is a **fear** that disrupts normal functioning and persists in the **absence of a direct threat;** symptoms include feelings of **fear, worry, tachycardia, hypertension, nausea, sleep disturbances** and **high glucocorticoid levels**
- these are the most prevalent of all psychiatric disorders; there are **four major classes** of anxiety:

  - **generalized anxiety** is a stress response in the absence of an obvious stimulus
  - **phobic anxiety** is caused by exposure to a **specific object** or situation (snakes, height etc.)
  - **panic disorders** are **rapid-onset attacks** characterized by extreme fear and stress symptoms (tachycardia, choking etc.)
- **obsessive-compulsive disorders** are **frequently recurring, uncontrollable** anxiety-producing thoughts and compensatory responses
- the role of **environmental stressors** is obvious in the etiology of anxiety disorders; however, there is also a **genetic contribution** as the concordance rate for identical twins is higher than for fraternal twins or siblings

b. Pharmacological Treatment of Anxiety Disorders

- treatment often includes **benzodiazepines** (Librium, Valium) that increase the binding of **GABA-A** to its receptors
- benzodiazepines are also clinically used as **hypnotics, muscle relaxants,** and **anticonvulsants;** problematic **side effects** include **tremors, nausea,** and **addiction**
- the efficacy of the new anxiolytic **buspirone**, which is an agonist at $5\text{-HT}_{1\text{-A}}$ **receptors,** suggests that **serotonergic systems** may also be involved in anxiety; this idea is supported by the fact that antidepressants that alter serotonergic function are also effective anxiolytics
- buspirone has many fewer side effects than benzodiazepines…it seems to be selective for anxiety, without producing ataxia, muscle relaxation, or sedation

    c.   **Neural Bases of Anxiety Disorders**

-   attention is being focused on brain structures such as the **amygdala**, due to the role that the amygdala plays in **fear and defensive behaviors**
-   the amygdala's high concentration of GABA-A receptors, and the fact that local infusions of benzodiazepines into the amygdala-producing anxiolytic effects in animals, and demonstrations that local injections of GABA antagonists into the amygdala can block the anxiolytic effects of systemic injections of benzodiazepines
-   brain imagines studies have not revealed any obvious brain pathology in patients suffering from anxiety disorders

2. **Tourette's Syndrome**

    a. **Symptoms and Etiology**

-   Tourette's syndrome (TS) is a disorder characterized by **tics,** or involuntary, repetitive movements or vocalizations
-   usually begins in **childhood;** symptoms become **progressively more complex** and severe with time
-   **common motor tics** include lewd gestures, hitting, touching, squatting, hopping and twirling
-   **common vocal tics** include barking, grunting, copralalia (uttering obscenities), and palilalia (repeating oneself)
-   TS is 3 times more likely in males than females; it has a major genetic component as there is a concordance rate of 55% for identical twins and 8% for fraternal twins
-   TS is often accompanied by **attention-deficit-hyperactivity disorder** or **obsessive-compulsive disorder**
-   the tics of TS can be suppressed for brief periods of time; however, during this time a tension builds up until released by a particularly intense period of tics

    b. **Brain Mechanisms and Treatment**

-   TS is a difficult disorder to study because there in no **good animal model** (making controlled experiments difficult); because the genetic basis is **unclear;** and because the tics that are symptomatic of the disorder make **imaging difficult** to conduct
-   two consistent results of brain imaging studies have been abnormalities in the **basal ganglia** and in the **limbic** and **association cortices**, leading researchers to believe that the neuropathology of TS may be due to alterations in neural circuits between the basal ganglia and cortex
-   treatment of TS typically begins by educating the patient and family about the disorder and dealing with the anxiety and depression that often accompanies it
-   the tics of TS are often treated with D-2 blocking **neuroleptic drugs**; this fact supports the idea that TS is due to a disorder of the basal ganglia, possibly excessive dopaminergic innervation of the striatum and associated limbic cortices

3. **Development of New Psychotherapeutic Drugs**

-   the development of new psychotherapeutic drugs is an exceedingly slow, expensive and complex task that begins with the **synthesis** of a new drug and the collection of **evidence from nonhuman subjects** to support its putative therapeutic efficacy
-   the importance of nonhuman subjects during this phase of drug development cannot be overestimated; without a solid foundation of comparative research, the development of drugs for human consumption is very difficulty
-   these initial steps take at least 5 years; if they are successful, the drug is eligible for **clinical trials** conducted on **human subjects** to assess the drug's safety and therapeutic efficacy

- clinical trials occur in **3 stages:**

  i)   **Screening for Safety**

  - this stage determines whether a drug is actually safe for humans and the dose range that can be tolerated; subjects are usually health, paid volunteers; this stage usually takes 18 months and costs $10,000,000 to complete

  ii)   **Establishing the Test Protocol:**

  - this established the conditions under which the final tests will be conducted; therapeutic dose, interdose interval, duration of drug treatment, likely benefits, and patients most likely to be helped are all determined
  - subjects are usually patients suffering from the disorder of interest and **placebo control groups**; the studies are usually done **double blind,** so that neither the subjects nor the attending physicians know which treatment a particular subject is getting
  - this phase normally takes about 2 years and costs about $20,000,000 to complete

  iii) **Final Tests**

  - this is typically a large, double-blind, placebo-controlled study involving thousands of patients suffering from the target disorder
  - often, **two independent tests** must be conducted to determine a successful drug candidate…that is, one that has greater therapeutic effects than noxious side effects
  - this phase normally takes 3.5 years and about $45,000,000 to complete

- the need for double-blind, placebo controlled studies means that some subjects, that might only recover from their illness if they receive the latest experimental treatment, will go untreated
- however, the only way that researchers can be sure a drug is effective is to control for the very real possibility of placebo effects in patients; if an **active placebo** is employed, that is even better
- the need for extensive testing of new drugs also means that it takes a long time for a drug to come to market…often frustrating patients and drug companies alike
- the amount of money required to develop a new drug means that drug costs are high, and many question the impartiality of clinical trials conducted by the drug companies themselves
- as Zivin (2000) has noted, **"Clinical trials can be trustworthy, fast, or cheap…but in any one trial, only 2 of the 3 are possible."** *THINK ABOUT IT!*

Suggested Websites for Lecture 18b

Anxiety Disorders: *http://anxiety.mentalhelp.net/*
  A page briefly explaining the symptoms and treatment of anxiety, with links to related sites.

National Anxiety Foundation: *http://lexington-on-line.com/naf.html*
  Home page for the National Anxiety Foundation; information on anxiety, panic attacks, OCD.

Tourette's Syndrome Association: *http://www.tsa-usa.org/*
  A good site for information about this psychological disorder.

NOTES

NOTES

NOTES

NOTES

NOTES

NOTES

NOTES

NOTES

NOTES

NOTES

NOTES